PELICAN BOOKS

A399

ATOMIC RADIATION AND LIFE

PETER ALEXANDER

PETER ALEXANDER

ATOMIC RADIATION AND LIFE

PENGUIN BOOKS

Penguin Books Ltd, Harmondsworth, Middlesex

U.S.A.: Penguin Books Inc., 3300 Clipper Mill Road, Baltimore 11, Md

AUSTRALIA: Penguin Books Pty Ltd, 762 Whitehorse Road, Mitcham, Victoria

—

First published 1957

Made and printed in Great Britain
by The Whitefriars Press Ltd
London and Tonbridge

To Professor Z. M. Bacq,
who introduced me to radiobiology,
in gratitude for his help and
many kindnesses

CONTENTS

ACKNOWLEDGEMENTS

I SHOULD like to thank the following for permission to reproduce illustrations:

Miss T. Alper for Plate 1a; The Atomic Research Establishment, Harwell, for Plate 2b; Professor P. C. Koller for Plates 3 and 7b; Dr S. H. Revell for Plates 5 and 7a; Dr E. H. Mercer and M. S. C. Birbeck for Plates 6a and b; Messrs Oliver and Boyd for Plate 8b, from *Edinburgh Medical Journal*, Vol. XLIX, No. 9, 1942; Commander R. A. Connard, U.S. Navy, for Plates 9a and b; *Radiology* and the authors for Plates 10b and 11, from an article by L. B. and W. L. Russell, in *Radiology*, Vol. 58, No. 3, 1952; Professor Åke Gustafsson for Plates 12a and b; Drs M. J. and O. G. Fahmy and K. Moreman for Plate 13; *The British Journal of Radiology* for Plate 14 (*left*); Metropolitan-Vickers Electrical Co. Ltd for Plate 14 (*right*); Atomic Energy of Canada Ltd for Plate 15; Dr R. J. King for Plate 16.

Messrs Methuen & Co. and the author for Figure 9, from Professor J. N. Davidson's *The Biochemistry of Nucleic Acids*; The McGraw-Hill Publishing Co. for Figure 11, after Cade, 1948, after Cauti and Spears, 1929, from *Radiation Biology* edited by Dr A. E. Hollaender; Dr A. C. Upton for Figures 20 and 31, from *Cancer Research*, Vol. 14, No. 9, 1954; Messrs Chapman and Hall for Figure 21, from Spear's *Radiations and Living Cells*; Dr Edith Paterson for Figure 22, from *British Journal of Radiology*, Vol. XXIX, No. 339; Dr R. A. M. Case for Figures 26, 27, 28, from *British Journal of Preventive and Social Medicine*, 1956, **10**, 172; Dr C. A. Tobias for Figure 30, from *Cancer Research*, 1956, **16**, 185; Dr L. H. Gray for Figure 38, from *British Journal of Radiology*, 1953, **26**, 609; Dr A. E. Hollaender for Figure 39, from *Journal of Cellular and Comparative Physiology*, 1953, **41**, 345; Dr L. A. Elson for Figure 24 from *Radiobiology Symposium* 1954 (Butterworth); Dr H. S. Kaplan for Figure 32 from *Journal of National Cancer Institute*, 1953, **14**, 303; Her Majesty's Stationery Office for Table x.

LIST OF PLATES

LIST OF TEXT FIGURES

FOREWORD

BY PROFESSOR ALEXANDER HADDOW, M.D., D.SC.

THE pioneer discoveries of Röntgen and Becquerel, made just over sixty years ago, set in motion a great chain of events the end of which no man can see. As with most scientific discoveries, they, and the spectacular increase in knowledge to which they led, can be applied for good or ill. They have already conferred signal benefits upon mankind. Equally, their application is fraught with much potential hazard: Pierre Curie, in his Nobel address as long ago as 1905, first referred to the danger which would confront humanity, were these powers to come into the hands of what he called 'les grands criminels'. In our own day, the revolutionary impact of nuclear science upon medicine and the public health, and upon industry, power, and warfare, has stimulated immense growth in the field of radiobiology, whether fundamental or applied. This is a meeting place of all the basic scientific disciplines, and to relate the story demands an exceptional breadth of understanding. To compass the task, no one is better qualified than Dr Alexander, whether on the grounds of his wide knowledge, or on those of the insight he has gained as one of the most vigorous experimentalists of the younger school. He has himself already made substantial contributions to our appreciation of the mode of action of ionizing radiations (especially in its chemical aspects), and of the ways in which the manifold biological effects can be on the one hand reproduced, and on the other prevented, by purely chemical means. At the same time he has already given many signs of his capacity to interpret the situation to a wider public. The present book is an outstanding example. In it he provides a conspectus of the physical qualities of the radiations involved, their action on matter, the chemistry thereof, and, lastly, their effects on the growth, division, ageing, hereditary mechanism, and mutation of the living cell. The work could scarcely be more timely, and will perform an invaluable service by its account not only of the facts but of their significance as well – a significance which grows from day to day, and which must, inevitably and increasingly, affect the future of our whole world.

Chester Beatty Research Institute,
Institute of Cancer Research: Royal Cancer Hospital,
London, S.W.3

INTRODUCTION

> To him who devotes his life to science nothing can give more happiness than making discoveries, but his cup of joy is full only when the results of his studies find practical application.
>
> PASTEUR

In 1936 a simple memorial was unveiled in Hamburg 'To the Röntgenologists and Radiologists of all nations who have given their lives in the struggle against the diseases of Mankind.' The names of 110 persons were inscribed initially and further additions have been made periodically as more deaths occur. These were the pioneers who immediately used for medical purposes the all-penetrating rays which had been discovered by the German physicist Wilhelm Konrad von Röntgen in 1895 at the University of Würzburg. This discovery opened a new era in medicine. The surgeon could see inside the body. Röntgen himself observed the bones of his living hand when he interposed this between the source of the X-rays and a screen which became luminescent on exposure to these rays. The bones attenuated the rays to a greater extent than did the surrounding flesh, and were thus revealed as dark areas on the screen. Application to surgical diagnosis followed rapidly and the technique was quickly introduced into England by Professor Silvanus Thompson. The early doctors, technicians, and nurses used these radiations without protecting themselves against them in any way, and some in their enthusiasm gave themselves tremendous exposures while demonstrating the method. They could not fail to notice that these radiations produced biological changes, but they shut their eyes to what seemed to be minor irritations, such as reddening of the skin, and carried on. Only when loss of hair was unambiguously correlated with exposure to X-rays was the biological hazard appreciated. But for most of the pioneers the warnings came too late, and almost without exception the early band of workers who persisted in practising radiography suffered a life of agony terminated by cancer. The injuries, usually starting in the hands (see Plate 8b), began with minor reddening round the fingernails and rapidly progressed to major deformations often involving whole limbs. Warts would form in large numbers and fuse into running sores; the condition was associated with continual pain. The final stage in these tragedies came many years after the firs exposures, when it was seen that cancers had developed at the site of the injuries. By 1909 it was firmly established that the dermatitis caused by repeated exposures to X-rays was frequently followed by the development of warts which eventually became cancers. Even when all exposure was stopped the changes continued, and cancer would occur between six and thirty years later. Great improvements in technique have removed all danger from the use of X-rays in radiodiagnosis, and both patient and operator are now completely safe (see, however, p. 91). Its role in modern medicine is known to everyone, since the 'taking of an X-ray' has become a routine; the possibility that the rapidly extending use of X-rays for diagnosis might present a long-term genetic danger is receiving very serious attention from the Medical Research Council (see p. 125).

The experience of the pioneer radiologists illustrates that the biological effects of atomic radiations and their dangers are nothing new. Indeed they have been studied intensively for sixty years. This is a fortunate circumstance, for if nuclear fission had been discovered without this background of knowledge its development as a new source of power would probably have taken a great toll of life. As it is, the need for strict precautions was well known, and we were fully forewarned about the possibility of long-delayed effects.

By a remarkable coincidence, within a year after Röntgen's discovery the French scientist Henri Becquerel found that uranium ores gave off penetrating radiations. This observation was the starting-point of the famous researches by Marie and Pierre Curie and Lord Rutherford, on which modern physics and chemistry are based. It was Becquerel himself who first observed that the radiations from radium gave rise to biological effects, when he noticed a burn on his skin nearest to the pocket in which he had carried a phial of radium. It was soon found that the radiations from this element were closely similar to X-rays and could also produce cancer. In fact, workers in mines rich in uranium had for generations been dying from a peculiar disease they named 'Bergkrankheit', but which has more recently been identified as lung cancer, caused by atomic radiations (see Chapter 5). Others who fell victims to cancer from radium were workers engaged in applying to watch and instrument dials paint rendered luminous by the addition of radioactive substances.

All these dangers are now fully appreciated, and it is unlikely that many workers were exposed to risk after 1930. The only large groups of people who have been affected by ionizing radiations in the last twenty-five years are the inhabitants of Hiroshima and Nagasaki, and more recently some natives in the Pacific islands close to the U.S. hydrogen weapon testing range. When the first of these was exploded in the spring of 1954, some 239 Marshall Islanders, the crew of a Japanese fishing trawler, and 28 American service men were exposed to fairly high doses of radiation from so-called radioactive fall-out which settled as a white dust. The only fatality was one of the fishermen, who died some time later; all the others have recovered from the so-called radiation sickness (see Chapter 3). It is however much too early to know whether any cancers will result, though past experience indicates that this is much to be feared. An increased cancer incidence in the survivors from the Hiroshima and Nagasaki atomic bombs is only now being noticed.

In spite of all the harm done, the biological effects of radiations, quite apart from their diagnostic application, have been turned decisively to man's advantage. Both X-rays and the radiations from radium were found to kill cells, and they were soon used in the treatment of cancer. This has proved to be a most difficult field, and after early jubilation its limitations have become recognized. There has been a steady improvement in technique over the last fifty years, and progress has been particularly rapid since artificial radioactive isotopes formed as by-products of nuclear energy have become available. Radiation therapy is playing a major role in the treatment of cancer and allied conditions, and has contributed largely to the marked improvements which have taken place. Many hundreds of thousands of lives must have been saved by atomic radiations.

All these considerations make radiobiology a subject of great interest, from both the scientific and practical point of view. In the last decade, however, the subject has received a new and much more powerful impetus, owing to the practical application of nuclear fission and the creation of a large atomic industry. It is planned that within the next twenty-five years a substantial proportion of all the electricity used in Britain will be obtained from atomic energy, and from now on almost all new power stations will be atomic. Radiobiology is therefore of direct concern to everyone. The possibility of exposure to atomic radiation is no longer confined to a few scientists and physicians. An ever-increasing number of people will be working in atomic industries, and problems such as the disposal of radioactive waste and adequate safeguards against accidents in atomic factories are a national concern. Regulations governing these hazards must be framed on an international level, since such factors as pollution of rivers or the sea cannot be confined within political boundaries. When considering the possible exposure of whole sections of the population, a new danger, relatively unimportant when only a few people were liable to exposure, comes into play. This is the so-called genetic damage which could lead to a dangerous increase in the number of live births of abnormal children, such as those suffering from mental defects. It is probably no exaggeration to say that radiation hazards will become one of the most important aspects of industrial and public hygiene. The medical officer of health of the future may spend as much of his time tracing radioactive contamination as he now does in detecting the sources of food poisoning.

The man in the street is confused about both the nature of the danger and its extent. Many conflicting and highly coloured statements have been made and have received wide publicity. It is hoped to describe here the many different aspects involved and to set the dangers in their true perspective. But a much more important aim of this book is to put before the general reader the scientific aspects of the biological changes produced by atomic radiation. This is a most fascinating subject, and the problem of how these radiations work is one of the great challenges to science. A great deal of work on it is now being done all over the world, and different facets are being attacked by some of the most able minds in science.

The study of radiobiology involves very many disciplines; physics, chemistry, biology, and the medical sciences are all concerned, and their interdependence adds to both the fascination and the difficulty of the subject. Highly specialized knowledge is required to determine the facts, but their interpretation requires a wide knowledge of all the different sciences concerned. Of necessity much of the background will here have to be presented too briefly and in an over-simplified form. The first chapter of this book may be rather heavy going for some, and in a first reading much of it can be skipped. But a true understanding of the biological change cannot be obtained without a knowledge of the basic physics, and I hope that readers will return to this chapter.

I have tried to trace the biological effects of the radiations step by step, from the injury to the cell to radiation sickness in the whole animal. We cannot follow as yet all the stages between the passage of the radiation through the irradiated organs and the final injury and we do not know what chemical changes intervene between the irradiation and the first biological damage. There are many clues, which are discussed in the final chapters, but the key discoveries have yet to be made. Herein lies the challenge and the fascination. There can be little doubt that once an understanding of the basic processes has been obtained, improvements in radiation therapy and in protection against the harmful effects of radiation will be rapid. The results of research in radiobiology also have an impact which extends far beyond the immediate problem of radiation damage. Much is being learned about the basic mechanisms of life, such as the biochemistry of cell division, by interfering with them by irradiation. By using atomic rays as probes with molecular dimensions much has already been discovered about viruses and related structures which form the transition between inanimate and living matter.

CHAPTER I

WHAT ARE ATOMIC RADIATIONS?

ATOMIC radiations, usually referred to as ionizing radiations, are essentially of two kinds: the electro-magnetic waves, known according to their origin as either X- or γ-rays, and subatomic particles, notably electrons, which move at very high speed. Although physically these two types of radiation are entirely different, their chemical and biological effects are closely similar and often identical, since they both knock out electrons from the atoms which make up the material through which they are passing. The loss of an electron confers high chemical reactivity on the atoms involved, and it is the subsequent reactions of these so-called ionized atoms which initiate the biological effects that are observed. From a biological point of view X- and γ-rays need be considered merely as a means of releasing high-energy electrons within the object which is being irradiated whatever its chemical constitution. Physically X- and γ-rays belong to the same class of radiation as light in the visible range, as well as the invisible infra-red or ultra-violet radiations, except that they are of very much shorter wavelength and this makes them much more energetic (see p. 28). All these radiations differ, however, completely, in the effects they produce in matter through which they pass, and only the energetic X- and γ-rays are able to strip off electrons from every type of atom to produce ions (see p. 15); the radiations of longer wavelengths produce, in general, only excitations (see p. 20).

The term γ-ray is used when the radiations are given off by radioactive substances, while they are called X-rays when produced in special high-voltage equipment. The γ-rays from radium, which until recently was the only powerful source, are of shorter wavelength than the X-rays produced in standard equipment, but this difference has disappeared with the development of super high-voltage machines which give X-rays which are more energetic (i.e. of shorter wavelength) than any γ-rays. To obtain a proper understanding of the way in which these radiations produce biological effects it is necessary to know in a little more detail what ionizations and excitations of molecules are. In the next section a brief summary description is given of the nature of matter and the properties of atoms. This is only the merest introduction which can do no more than remind the reader of things he once knew but has forgotten.

THE ATOM

All matter is made up of atoms, the structure of which was revealed by brilliant experimentation with atomic radiations; in this British physicists, notably Lord Rutherford and Sir J. J. Thomson, played an outstanding part. From the way in which these radiations interact with the material through which they pass, it was concluded that atoms are made up of an inner nucleus – much smaller than the whole atom – surrounded by electrons which move in orbits. Almost the whole mass of the atom is concentrated in the nucleus, which is positively charged; overall electrical neutrality being maintained by the circulating electrons, whose total negative electric charge exactly neutralizes the charge of the nucleus. Fig. 1 shows in a purely diagrammatic form how the structure of an atom of carbon may be imagined.

The constitution of the atomic nucleus, and in particular the forces which hold it together, are the outstanding problem of contemporary physics. It seems certain that the nucleus is made up of protons and neutrons. The mass of both these particles on an atomic scale is called one, but the proton carries a positive charge of exactly the same magnitude as the negative charge of the electron, while the neutron is electrically uncharged. The weight of an electron is only 1/1800 part of that of a proton, which explains why the mass of an atom is almost wholly contained in the nucleus. In macroscopic terms a proton is an extremely small entity weighing $1{\cdot}66 \times 10^{-24}$ g.* Similarly the electric charge of an electron or proton, which is simply referred to as -1 or $+1$ respectively, is also minute. Thus in a wire carrying current of 1 ampere, $6{\cdot}25 \times 10^{18}$ electrons pass every second, or the charge of an electron $= 1{\cdot}6 \times 10^{-19}$ ampere-seconds. Whenever weight or electric charges are referred to without units they are always based on the atomic scale

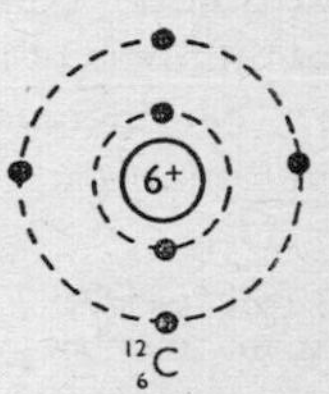

Hydrogen Atom
nuclear charge + 1
nuclear weight 1
one outer electron shell contains one electron and needs two to be in stable form.

Carbon Atom
nuclear charge + 6
nuclear weight of most common isotope 12
one outer electron shell has four electrons and needs eight to be in stable form.

Fig. 1 – Diagrammatic representation of the structure of atoms.

where a proton has a mass of 1 and a charge of + 1. The charge of the nucleus, which must be the same as the total number of external electrons, is the same as the atomic number, and the weight of the nucleus determines the atomic weight.

Isotopes. The chemical behaviour of an element is entirely determined by the number of the external electrons surrounding the nucleus and their distribution in the different orbits. The actual mass of the nucleus does not influence the

* 28 g. are approximately equal to one ounce. Another weight used is 1 mg. = 1/1000 g. The shorthand notation using exponents is extremely useful when either very small or very large numbers are being dealt with; 3×10^3 means the same thing as $3 \times 1{,}000$, 3×10^{17} is $3 \times$ (1 with 17 zeros); $3 \times 10^{-3} = 0{\cdot}003$ and $3 \times 10^{-17} = 0\cdot$ (16 zeros) 3.

chemical reactivity of the atoms, and almost every element found in nature is composed of a number of atoms of different atomic weights with the same atomic number (i.e. having nuclei of different weight but the same charge, and of course the same number of external electrons). These different atomic species are referred to as isotopes of the same element; an element being characterized by its atomic number. It is generally believed that the nuclei of the different isotopes contain the same number of protons, but different numbers of neutrons. These, being uncharged, but of mass 1, can increase the atomic weight without changing the atomic number. The usual way of describing different isotopes is

$$\frac{\text{Atomic weight}}{\text{Atomic number}}\text{(chemical symbol for element).}$$

For instance $^{36}_{17}Cl$ is the chlorine isotope of atomic weight 36. The chlorine found in nature has an atomic weight of 35·5 and is composed of approximately equal quantities of $^{35}_{17}Cl$ and $^{36}_{17}Cl$. Isotopes of the same element are extremely difficult to separate, since their chemical reactions are identical, and only properties which depend on the weight of the atoms, such as rate of diffusion, can be used for their isolation. The separation of the fissionable uranium isotope $^{235}_{92}U$ from uranium found in nature is one of the most important processes in the development of atomic energy. Natural uranium is made up predominantly of the isotope $^{238}_{92}U$ but contains also in small amounts the isotopes $^{235}_{92}U$ and $^{234}_{92}U$. The successful isolation of $^{235}_{92}U$ on a large scale represents a major triumph of chemical engineering.

The subatomic particles. The particles with which we are chiefly concerned in this book are electrons, protons, neutrons, and alpha (α) particles. The latter are the nuclei of the element helium without its external electrons. Helium has an atomic number of two and an atomic weight of four (i.e. $^{4}_{2}He$) and an α-particle has therefore a weight of four and a charge of + 2. A hydrogen atom is $^{1}_{1}H$, and a proton can therefore also be considered as a hydrogen nucleus. An isotope of hydrogen $^{2}_{1}H$ is usually called deuterium, and when it loses its external electron it becomes a subatomic particle, known as a deuterium ion of mass 2 and charge + 1.*

All the subatomic particles when moving at high speed (i.e. when of high energy) can pass through matter. The depth of penetration depends on their speed and charge – the higher the charge the smaller the penetration. In their passage through matter they knock out electrons from atoms, and are therefore called ionizing radiations. High speed electrons are for convenience called beta (β)-rays. Until recently the only source of such high-energy radiations was the radioactive isotopes (see p. 6), but a number of high-voltage machines have now been designed which can accelerate atomic particles until they have the velocities, or energies, necessary for penetrating deeply. These machines are being used to an increasing extent in hospitals for the treatment of deep-seated cancers. The energy of these radiations is expressed in a special unit known as the electron-volt† (eV) and the multiples 1,000 eV = 1 keV; 1,000 keV = 1 MeV.

RADIOACTIVITY

The nuclei of certain isotopes are unstable and eject subatomic particles, usually electrons and occasionally alpha-particles. These nuclear rearrangements are very frequently

* In the last few years it has become possible to strip some or all of the external electrons from certain heavier elements. One which has been used for biological experiments is carbon ($^{12}_{6}C$) without its electrons. It gives a particle of mass 12 and charge + 6. These particles are unlikely to play an important role in therapy or as a radiation hazard except perhaps at high altitudes where pilots may encounter a very few such particles in the stratosphere. They come in from outer space, but are very readily stopped by air, and cannot pass through the atmosphere to reach the earth's surface. These heavy and highly charged particles are likely to be extremely damaging to tissue and the possibility that they may affect pilots is receiving attention.

† 1 eV corresponds to $1{\cdot}60 \times 10^{-12}$ ergs; $4{\cdot}2 \times 10^{7}$ ergs = 1 calorie, 800 calories = 1 h.p. (horse-power), or 1 h.p. = $2{\cdot}1 \times 10^{22}$ eV.

TABLE I

Examples of radioactive rearrangements

A. Emission of an electron (β^-) only

$$^{14}_{6}C \xrightarrow{\beta^-} {}^{14}_{7}N$$ half-life 5,570 years
energy of β^- 0·15 MeV

B. Electron emission as well as γ-rays

$$^{203}_{80}Hg \xrightarrow[\gamma]{\beta^-} {}^{203}_{81}Te$$ half-life 48 days; $\beta^- = 0{\cdot}2$ MeV
$\gamma = 0{\cdot}28$ MeV

$$^{60}_{27}Co \xrightarrow[\gamma_1, \gamma_2]{\beta^-} {}^{60}_{28}Ni$$ half-life 5·3 years; $\beta^- = 0{\cdot}3$ MeV
$\gamma_1 = 1{\cdot}3$ MeV
$\gamma_2 = 1{\cdot}2$ MeV

(two quanta of γ-rays differing slightly in energy are given off on each disintegration).

$^{60}_{27}Co$ (radioactive cobalt) is used as a source for high energy γ-rays since the electrons (β^-) can be stopped by a thin film of metal which does not significantly stop the γ-rays. When ^{60}Co is used for medical treatment only the γ-rays are active.

C. Alternative rearrangements possible

$$^{130}_{55}Cs \xrightarrow{\beta^-} {}^{130}_{56}Ba$$ half-life 30 minutes

$$^{130}_{55}Cs \xrightarrow{\beta^+} {}^{130}_{54}Xe$$

(three entirely different elements all having the same molecular weight).

D. Emits γ-rays only. This means that no chemical change has occurred and only the energy level of the nucleus is altered.

$$^{135}_{56}Ba \xrightarrow{\gamma} {}^{135}_{56}Ba$$ half-life 29 hours.

E. Emission of α-particle

$$^{210}_{84}Po \xrightarrow{\alpha} {}^{206}_{82}Pb$$ half-life 140 days ; $\alpha = 5{\cdot}3$ MeV

accompanied by the emission of γ-rays of varying wavelength, and Table I shows some typical radioactive rearrangements. After a nucleus has given off an electron (i.e. the isotope is called a β-emitter) its atomic number is increased by one, since the positive charge on the nucleus is

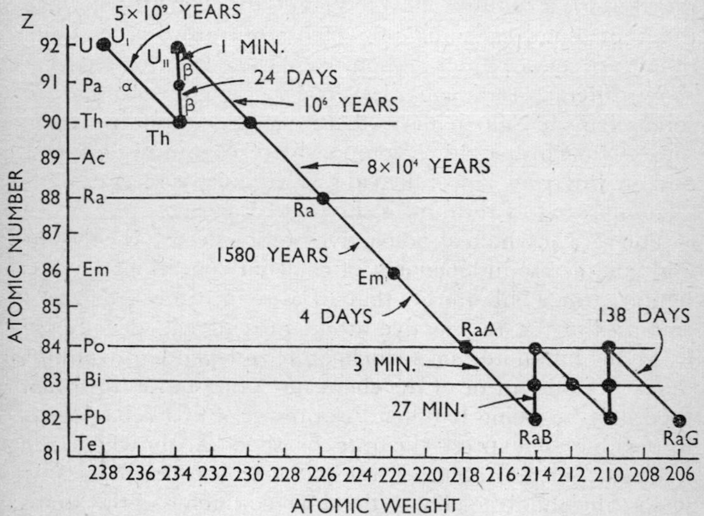

Fig. 2 – Radioactive decay series. Uranium (At. Wt. 238) decays very slowly with emission of an α-particle to give Thorium 234. This then emits an electron (β-ray) twice in succession till a different Uranium isotope is reached, which in turn gives off α-particles, and so on until the process finishes with lead (Pb) of atomic weight 206, which is a stable atom and which does not undergo further change. The values for the 'half lives' of the different steps are given in the diagram.

thereby increased; the atomic weight however remains unaltered. In the case of an alpha-emitter the atomic number of the isotope is decreased by two and its atomic weight by four, since it has lost a particle of charge + 2 and weight four. The chemical nature of an atom after undergoing radioactive change is always entirely altered, since as a result of changing its atomic number it has become a different element. It must be stressed that radioactivity is entirely concerned with the nucleus, and that the external electrons which determine the chemical behaviour of the atom play no part. Consequently the radioactivity of an isotope is quite independent of its chemical constitution, and the emission of β-rays, for example, is the same for radium metal as for a radium salt. Frequently an element will have different isotopes, some of which are radioactive while others are stable; different isotopes of the same element may show different radioactivities. The radioactive isotopes of some elements, particularly those of high atomic number, may change into another isotope which is again radioactive, and in this way a so-called decay series arises. A typical example, that of radium, is shown in Fig. 2.

The rate at which a radioactive isotope decays is constant and completely independent of external conditions such as temperature. This means that in a given time a constant *proportion* of the radioactive atoms present will decompose by giving off an atomic particle quite independently of how many are present or of the chemical combination in which the isotope is being handled. As a result of this behaviour it is possible to express the rate or speed with which the nucleus of an unstable (i.e. radioactive) isotope changes by its so-called half-life. This is the time in which half the atoms present will have changed. A typical decay curve is shown in Fig. 3. The rate at which the nuclei disintegrate varies widely, and the half-life of some isotopes is a fraction of a second while that of others is millions of years; the values for the radium series of isotopes are seen in Fig. 2.

Natural radioactivity. All the different radioisotopes in a decay series, such as that shown in Fig. 2, are present in nature, since they are continually being formed and broken down. The relative amount depends on their rate of disintegration, and those having a short half-life will only be present in very minute amounts. Thus in the course of their isolation of radium from the uranium ore, pitchblende, the Curies discovered polonium, an isotope with a relatively short half-life of 138 days, which was present in much smaller amounts than radium of 1,580 years half-life. There are other radioactive decay series in addition to the uranium-radium series, and all these contribute radioactive isotopes which occur in nature. Although the parent

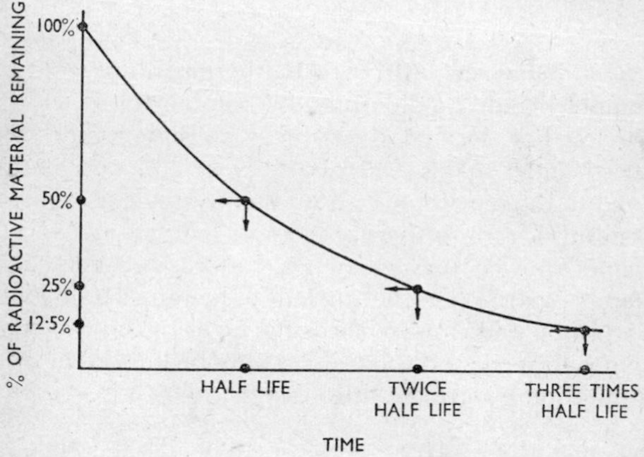

Fig. 3 – The rate at which a radioactive material decays. The half life of an isotope is the time required for one half of all the atoms which were originally present to have decayed.

member of the uranium-radium series ($^{238}_{92}U$) and of the thorium series ($^{232}_{90}Th$) are present in very large amounts on the earth they are extremely stable, having half-lives of 5×10^9 and $1{\cdot}6 \times 10^{10}$ years respectively, so that the amount of radioactivity from them is very small, and it is the accumulation of their less stable decay products which provides us with the bulk of the naturally occurring radioactivity found on this planet. In addition to these isotopes, all of which originate from, and are elements of, high molecular weight, the low molecular weight element potassium contains a radioactive isotope, $^{40}_{19}K$, which makes up approximately 0·1 per cent of all the potassium found in nature. This isotope also has an extremely long half-life,

1·3 × 10⁹ years, and decays to give the stable isotope of calcium, $^{40}_{20}Ca$. Since it is very common and widespread, and moreover makes up of the order of 3×10^{-4} per cent of the body of all mammals, this isotope contributes significantly to the total amount of ionizing radiation to which the body is continually exposed.* This is discussed in detail on p. 123.

Artificial radioactivity. In 1919 Rutherford discovered that stable nuclei could be disrupted by bombardment with fast α-particles. For the first time nuclear disintegrations were produced under man's control and were no longer entirely confined to the inevitable and unalterable events associated with natural radioactive processes. Rutherford and his colleagues showed that when light atoms are bombarded with an α-particle (i.e. the nucleus of helium $^{4}_{2}He$) they will emit a proton and capture the α-particle. In this way a new element is formed, and the process may be illustrated by the transmutation of nitrogen into oxygen, which is written:

$$^{14}_{7}N + \underset{(\alpha\text{-particle})}{^{4}_{2}He} + \longrightarrow {}^{17}_{8}O + \underset{(\text{proton})}{^{1}_{1}H}$$

A rather rare isotope of oxygen is formed which is present to the extent of 1 part in 3,150 in normal oxygen. These artificial transmutations are however rare and confined to the lightest elements, because both the α-particles and the nucleus are positively charged and therefore repel one another. The α-particles must be sufficiently energetic to overcome the repulsion, and the energy of the α-particles available from the natural radioactive isotopes is sufficient only for entering nuclei of elements of low atomic number

* In ordinary hydrogen there is a very rare isotope known as tritium which is present only to the extent of one part in 10^{18}. It is hydrogen of atomic weight 3, $^{3}_{1}H$ and gives off very weak β-rays. Although its half-life is only 11·8 years, it does not contribute a significant amount to the radiation ordinarily received, since it is present only in such minute amounts.

which carry the smallest nuclear charge.* Clearly protons and deuterons which carry only one positive charge will be able to enter a nucleus with lower energies than the doubly charged α-particles. Since no radioisotopes emit protons and deuterons the use of these particles for effecting nuclear changes had to await the construction of high-voltage equipment, and was first achieved by Cockcroft and Walton in 1932. They thus realized the alchemists' dream of changing one element into another under conditions created entirely by the experimenter. In all these experiments the transmutations gave rise to stable nuclei, but in 1934 Mme. and M. Joliot-Curie discovered a new phenomenon of fundamental importance. By bombarding different elements with α-particles in the same way as Rutherford and Chadwick had done they found that they could produce new isotopes which were themselves unstable and gave off atomic particles with different half-lives. These laboratory-produced unstable isotopes were in every respect similar to naturally occurring radioactive materials. This basic discovery was not of any practical importance for the production of radioactive materials, since the quantities formed were unbelievably minute: the techniques of the atomic physicist make it possible to detect and measure the radioactivity from a single atom. The use of high-energy protons and deuterons produced in high-voltage equipment made the production of artificial radioisotopes much easier, and in the same year as the Joliot-Curies' discovery, Cockcroft and Walton produced radioactive nitrogen. But their technique is also limited essentially to the bombardment of light elements, and of these only very small quantities can be produced even with present-day high-voltage equipment. The preparation of the large quantities of isotopes now used

* Electrons which carry a charge opposite to that of the nucleus are repelled by the external electrons and can penetrate to the nucleus only if they have extremely high energies in excess of most of the β-rays given off by the natural radioactive elements. Within the last ten years the development of high-voltage equipment has made it possible to obtain electrons of sufficient energy to produce transmutations which often lead to the formation of artificially radioactive isotopes.

for therapeutic, diagnostic, and research purposes in medicine and for many industrial purposes had to await two further discoveries; the use of neutrons for transmutation and the formation of large quantities of neutrons in the piles in which atomic energy is generated.

The neutrons. While Chadwick was studying the disintegration of atoms with α-particles in 1933, he revolutionized our concept of matter by the discovery of a new entity without charge, but having the same mass as the proton. This particle, the neutron ($^{1}_{0}n$), is now believed to be one of the major components of the nuclei of atoms, and is the ideal particle for disintegrating nuclei since it carries no charge and will therefore not be repelled. The Italian physicist Fermi immediately recognized the great potentialities of neutrons for the bombardment of the heavier elements to give unstable (i.e. radioactive) nuclei, and as early as 1934 he published his discovery that of the sixty elements which were exposed to neutrons, forty gave rise to radioactive isotopes, none of which existed in nature. The ease with which different isotopes capture neutrons is defined by the so-called neutron cross-section and varies greatly.* In the course of these transformations either α-particles, electrons, or protons are usually given off, and all these possibilities are realized when aluminium is bombarded.

This reaction illustrates the multiplicity of products which are obtained and which in this case are all artificial β-emitters.

(1) $^{27}_{13}Al + ^{1}_{0}n \longrightarrow ^{28}_{13}Al$
$^{28}_{13}Al \longrightarrow ^{28}_{14}Si + e^{-}$ (half-life 2·3 min.)

* A very few nuclei, notably the uranium isotope $^{235}_{92}U$, will on capturing a neutron break up completely and give off two or more neutrons. In this way chain reaction can be set up, which if allowed to proceed without check, gives rise to an explosion – the atom bomb. The same isotopes, referred to as fissionable, also form the basic constituents of the atomic reactors or piles where the excess neutrons from, for example, $^{235}_{92}U$ are captured by other isotopes such as the abundant $^{238}_{92}U$ to give more fissionable material. In this way atomic energy is released in a ontrolled and useful form.

(2) $^{27}_{13}Al + ^{1}_{0}n \longrightarrow ^{27}_{12}Mg + ^{1}_{1}H$
$^{27}_{12}Mg \longrightarrow ^{27}_{13}Al + e^{-}$ (half-life 10 min.)

(3) $^{27}_{13}Al + ^{1}_{0}n \longrightarrow ^{24}_{11}Na + ^{4}_{2}He$
$^{24}_{11}Na \longrightarrow ^{24}_{12}Mg + e^{-}$ (half-life 15 hours)

The stage was thus set for the preparation of synthetic radioactive materials from almost every element and with an enormous range of half-lives. Isotopes can now be prepared which give off electrons (β-rays) and γ-rays ranging in energy from a few thousand to many million electron-volts, but they could not be prepared in large quantities until a rich source of neutrons became available. Originally neutrons were obtained as a by-product of bombardment of light elements with α-particles from naturally occurring radioactive materials, but in this way only minute quantities of isotopes could be produced. The pile or reactor used for atomic energy production solved the problem of a neutron source and the vast majority of isotopes used for practical purposes are now prepared by irradiation in the pile.

Fortunately for the free world Fermi left Italy as a refugee from fascism and was thus able to contribute to the Allied atomic energy project in World War II. He was one of the guiding spirits in the construction of the first atomic pile in Chicago which started to work in 1942. The story of the artificial radio-isotopes, starting with Rutherford's concept of atomic transmutations to their successful large-scale production as an adjunct to atomic energy, represents one of the greatest achievements of science, and some of the principal participants, Chadwick, Cockcroft, and Joliot-Curie, are still active. Fermi died at the age of 54 in 1953 of leukaemia almost certainly contracted as the result of exposure to ionizing radiations.

The application of these isotopes in medicine has already led to great advances in diagnosis and treatment, but mankind may in the long run derive the greatest gain from the application of the isotopes to research. Their use makes it possible to study the details of intricate biological and metabolic processes in a way which would not otherwise have been possible. This aspect falls outside the scope of this book, in which the radioactive isotopes will be considered merely as sources of ionizing radiation.

STOPPING OF IONIZING RADIATIONS BY MATTER

The corpuscular radiations (electrons, protons, α-particles, etc.) given off by radioactive materials or generated in high-voltage equipment move at extremely high speeds, often close to that of light.* Their velocity is determined by their energy, expressed in electron-volts (eV) (see footnote on p. 5), a unit which is particularly convenient when dealing with beams of electrons (i.e. β-rays) since it is numerically equal to the voltage used to accelerate them to the required speed. The heavier particles move much more slowly than electrons of the same energy (see Fig. 5).

Since matter is made up of positively charged atomic nuclei and negatively charged electrons, it is clear that the electrically charged corpuscular particles must interact with the atoms in the molecules which surround their path. It is very rare for heavy particles, such as protons or α-particles, to hit an atomic nucleus† or for electrons (β-rays) to collide with the orbital electrons. When such a collision has occurred the particles involved change direction. Except when scattered in this way the subatomic particles move through matter, gas, liquid, or solid, in straight lines. However, even when they do not come into physical contact with atoms they are continually slowed down by the local electric charges of the atoms, rather as air resistance will

* The speed of light in a vacuum, 186,000 miles per second, is the upper limit at which any particle can move. No particle, however energetic, can actually attain this velocity, but at high energies they come very close to it.

† The observation, made by Rutherford in 1908, that on passing a beam of α-particles through a very thin metal foil a small fraction of them became deflected provided the first and most decisive evidence for the postulate that the total mass of atoms is concentrated within a small positively charged nucleus which occupies only a minute fraction of the total volume.

slow down a bullet. Because of the electrical interactions with the atoms through which they pass they lose energy until they can penetrate no further. At the very end of their tracks the path of the particles is no longer linear, since scattering occurs much more readily when they move relatively slowly (see Plate 1). The energy which the ionizing particles lose is taken up by the surrounding atoms, and some of the molecules of which they are part become *chemically* changed. It is this radiochemical process which is responsible for the biological effects produced. Only a part of the energy lost in this way is used for producing such chemical changes. Much of the energy is dissipated as heat, though this does not bring about any of the observed biological changes, since a radiation dose sufficient to kill a mammal would raise its temperature by less than one hundredth of a degree.

IONIZATION, EXCITATION, AND FREE RADICALS

The energy transferred by the atomic particle to the surrounding matter brings about ionization of atoms and excitation of molecules. In an ionization an atom loses one of its external electrons and thus becomes positively charged since the atomic nucleus remains unaltered. The electron which is ejected has only a small amount of energy and in all biological systems is quickly taken up in the outer electron shell of another atom to form a negatively charged molecule. In the case of water this process may be written as follows:

$$H_2O \xrightarrow{\text{irradiated}} H_2O^+ + e$$

$$H_2O + e \longrightarrow H_2O^-$$

$$\text{or overall effect} \quad 2H_2O \longrightarrow H_2O^+ + H_2O^-$$

Molecules with atoms which have either lost or gained an electron are called ions, but they are in addition free radicals, which confers on them extremely high chemical reactivity, and ions such as H_2O^+ and H_2O^- rapidly undergo further changes. The biological effects of radiations depend largely on the reactions of free radicals, and in order to understand them one must have some idea of the principles which determine the formation of chemical compounds.

To put it very briefly and simply: with very few exceptions atoms do not exist as such in nature, but are found in combination as molecules, held together by the interaction between the outer electrons which are arranged round the atomic nucleus in a number of orbits technically known as shells. The maximum number of electrons which can be accommodated in any one shell is limited. Thus in the case of hydrogen (^1_1H), the lightest element with atomic number 1, we have only one external electron which moves in the first shell. The next element, helium, accommodates its two electrons in the same shell, but this represents the maximum number for this inner orbit. The next higher elements fill out the next shell, which can accommodate up to eight electrons. Oxygen, which has the atomic number 8, has two electrons in its innermost shell and six electrons in the next shell. As the atomic number rises more shells are filled, and some of these can contain up to thirty-two electrons; however, as we go from one element to the next the shells are not necessarily completely filled before electrons appear in the next one. Now atoms are most stable when they have eight electrons in their outermost shell, with the exception of hydrogen and helium, which are quite stable if they have two electrons. Only six elements have this stable configuration, and these are the only elements which exist as individual atoms in nature; they are known as the inert gases, since they are chemically completely unreactive. All other atoms strive to attain an outer shell containing eight electrons (or in the case of hydrogen two electrons); this they can do in two ways, either by exchanging or by sharing electrons. Sodium chloride is an example of exchanging; the eleven electrons of sodium (atomic number 11) are arranged as follows: two electrons in the first shell, eight in the second, and one in the third; this is written, 2, 8, 1. By losing the outermost electron and becoming a so-called positively charged ion (Na^+) it has the stable and unreactive octet structure: 2, 8. Chlorine (atomic number 17) has the electronic configuration 2, 8, 7; energetically it is quite impossible for it to lose seven electrons, and it achieves the electron octet by gaining one electron to become the negative ion Cl^- with a 2, 8, 8, arrangement in its orbit.

$$Na + Cl \dashrightarrow Na^+ \; Cl^-$$

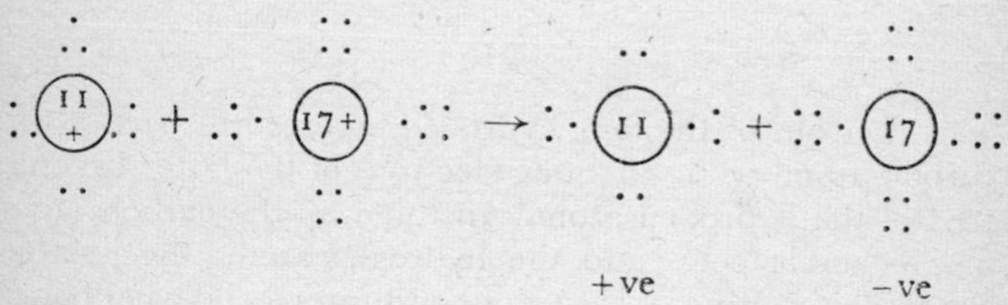

(11+) + (17+) → (11) + (17)

+ve −ve

(Dots represent outer electrons which neutralize the positive charge of the nucleus.)

These ions, apart from the fact that they carry an electric charge, are extremely stable and entirely different, chemically, from their parent elements. Common salt is made up of sodium and chloride ions, and is known as an ionic molecule; as such it is quite unreactive, but elementary chlorine is a poison gas, and sodium combines so violently with water that it catches alight. So it can be seen that the chemical properties of an atom are determined by the outer electrons only, and are quite independent of the nucleus. Conversely the radioactivity of an atom is entirely independent of the arrangements of these electrons.

Another way of obtaining a stable configuration is for atoms to share their electrons, and in this way covalent molecules are formed. All molecules containing carbon are of this type, since this element has four electrons in its outer shell (2, 4). To gain or lose four electrons and become a tetra- negatively or positively charged ion respectively is energetically almost impossible,* and carbon compounds

* Such ions have in fact only been produced very recently in very high-voltage machines known as cyclotrons.

therefore share electrons with other atoms. If we represent the four outer electrons of carbon by dots, thus $\cdot\overset{\cdot}{\underset{\cdot}{\mathrm{C}}}\cdot$, and a hydrogen atom with its one electron thus, H $\times$, the very stable gas methane (CH_4) can be written

$$\begin{array}{ccc} & \mathrm{H} & \\ & \cdot\times & \\ \mathrm{H}\ \overset{\times}{\cdot} & \mathrm{C} & \overset{\cdot}{\times}\ \mathrm{H} \\ & \times\cdot & \\ & \mathrm{H} & \end{array}$$

The electrons of the four hydrogen atoms form part of the carbon atom, while the four electrons of the latter become part of the hydrogen atoms. In this way the carbon atom has its stable octet and the hydrogen atoms their stable pairs. This sharing of electrons constitutes a chemical bond. Elements such as hydrogen H or Cl exist in nature as molecules of two atoms H_2 or Cl_2 which have a stable structure by sharing electrons with one another; e.g. Cl_2 is

$$\begin{array}{ccccc} & \cdot\ \cdot & & \times\times & \\ \vdots & \mathrm{Cl} & \overset{\cdot}{\times} & \mathrm{Cl} & \overset{\times}{\times} \\ & \cdot\ \cdot & & \times\times & \end{array}$$

Oxygen has six electrons in its outer shell, and consequently can form an octet with two hydrogen atoms to give the molecule water $\begin{array}{ccc} & \mathrm{H} & \\ & \cdot\times & \\ \vdots & \mathrm{O} & \overset{\cdot}{\times}\ \mathrm{H} \\ & \cdot\ \cdot & \end{array}$ Now this structure can dissociate into two *stable* ions H^+ and OH^-. H^+, the hydrogen ion, is the same thing as a proton and has no electrons. In the hydroxyl ion both atoms by sharing electrons have stable configurations, i.e. $\begin{array}{ccc} & \mathrm{H} & \\ & \cdot\times & \\ \vdots & \mathrm{O} & \vdots \\ & \cdot\ \cdot & \end{array}$ but this entity has one more orbital electron than positive nuclear charges and therefore carries an overall negative charge.

Free radicals. Ionizing radiations produce very reactive structures which are known as free radicals, and some of their reactions will be discussed in more detail in Chapter 8. Essentially they are structures in which each of the atoms does not have a stable electron arrangement. The simplest example is a hydrogen atom, H, which is tremendously reactive because it tends to become stabilized either by sharing an electron with another atom or by losing its sole electron to become a hydrogen ion. Free radicals can exist only for an extremely short period; their 'life time' depends on the nature and concentration of other substances present, but in general lasts only for a minute fraction of a second before undergoing some chemical reaction. In the case of a hydrogen atom the simplest reaction is for two of them to combine to give a stable molecule of hydrogen. A free radical important in radiobiology is the hydroxyl radical; this is a hydroxyl ion which has lost one electron

$$\begin{array}{c} H \\ \cdot \\ :\,O\,: \\ \cdot\,\cdot \end{array}$$

thereby becoming electrically neutral again but highly reactive. Since free radicals are characterized by having an odd electron they are written with a dot (e.g. $OH^{\cdot}$). The ions formed by the atomic radiations are not those normally encountered (e.g. in a solution of common salt where we have Na^+ and Cl^-), but free radicals. For example, in neither of the two ions formed by irradiation of water

$$\begin{array}{c} \cdot\,\cdot \\ H \overset{\cdot}{\times} O \overset{\cdot}{\times} H \\ \cdot \\ H_2O^+ \end{array} \qquad\qquad \begin{array}{c} \cdot\,\cdot \\ H \overset{\cdot}{\times} O \overset{\cdot}{\times} H \\ \cdot\,\cdot \\ \cdot \\ H_2O^- \end{array}$$

is the oxygen atom surrounded by an octet of electrons.

Excitation. Besides actually removing electrons from their orbits to produce atoms deficient in an electron (i.e. a positively charged radical) atomic particles can also alter the arrangement of the electrons within their orbits. This process is known as 'excitation' since it increases the chemical reactivity of these molecules without producing a free radical or ion. The degree of electronic excitation can be varied widely, and is dependent on the extent to which the electrons have been disturbed. A molecule cannot remain in an excited state for an appreciable time – often this period is less than that of a free radical – and if in its lifetime it has not undergone a reaction the electrons will return to their most stable arrangement and the molecule will be back in its original state.

THE WILSON CLOUD CHAMBER

Although the subatomic particles are much too minute to be seen, there are a number of ways by which the tracks along which they have travelled can be made visible. The 'footprints' which reveal their presence are the ionizations of the atoms lying within their path. Ionization can result in the fogging of a photographic plate, and this was the effect which led to the original discovery of radioactivity by Henri Becquerel in 1892. Recently this photographic method has been greatly refined and the tracks of individual particles can now be revealed as they cross the film. Another way of rendering the particles visible is to direct them against a luminescent screen which will give off a flash of visible light whenever it is hit by a sufficiently energetic particle. In early work with α-rays this method was used to prove that these rays consisted of distinct particles.

The bulk of our information as to what happens when ionizing radiations pass through matter is obtained from an ingenious device known as the Cloud Chamber, devised by C. T. R. Wilson at Cambridge. The reason why a mist of water droplets is formed when a humid atmosphere is suddenly cooled is that the amount of water vapour which a given volume of gas can hold decreases as the temperature is lowered. On cooling a gas saturated with water vapour, droplets cannot form unless there are centres on which water molecules can collect; in their absence the gas continues to hold the moisture, but will release it as soon as impurity centres are introduced. Ions formed by atomic radiations can act as foci for the precipitation of drops from so-called supersaturated vapours. In a Wilson cloud chamber a saturated atmosphere of water vapour is suddenly cooled and the path of a charged particle will be marked by a line of fine water droplets which can be photographed. Under suitable conditions each ion formed will give rise to a droplet. Plate 1 shows the tracks of different particles obtained in this way.

From Plate 1b it can be seen that a 1 MeV electron as it passes through the supersaturated atmosphere produces clusters of droplets separated by a gap. One would of course expect to find clusters of two droplets, since an ion pair is invariably formed; one ion by the ejection of an electron (e.g. the positive ion H_2O^+) and another by the capture of this electron to give a negative ion. These two events cannot be separated, and one always refers to the production of ion pairs by these radiations. A notable feature, however, is that there are many clusters which contain more than two droplets. These arise from the fact that the fast-moving electron can expel electrons from the molecules through which it passes at all speeds from zero to that at which it is itself travelling. It happens fairly frequently that the electron ejected in forming a positive ion is itself capable of producing further ionizations. These clusters contain the two droplets originating from the ion pairs produced by the energetic β-ray itself as well as a variable number of additional droplets due to ionization brought about by the ejected electron. The energy of the latter is usually too small for it to give rise to a distinct track of its own, and it is seen as a cluster. On the occasions when it is relatively energetic it gives rise to short tracks which can be seen as spurs sticking out from the main track and are known as δ-rays. This behaviour is shown clearly in the case of an α-particle in Plate 1a. There is no clear dividing line between a short δ-ray and a cluster.

As already mentioned, atomic radiations in addition to removing electrons from atoms also transfer energy to atoms by disturbing the electronic arrangements, and produce an excited atom. Excitations are certainly much more frequent than ionization, but they cannot readily be revealed, and are not shown in cloud chamber photographs. To obtain a clear representation of what happens in the path of a β-ray we should have to include an unknown number of excitations in between each set of clusters.

THE RANGE OF IONIZING PARTICLES

In Plate 1c the tracks of a slow and a moderately fast electron are superimposed; apart from the obvious difference that the particle of low energy no longer moves in a straight line as the result of scattering it also produces many more ions along a given length of track. The droplets originating from single ions or even ion clusters can no longer be distinguished, since they are too close together. In other words the ion density along the track of a slow (i.e. low energy) electron is greater than that of a fast electron. This difference is even more marked when we compare electrons with heavier particles, such as protons or α-particles (see Plate 1a). These heavy particles produce extremely high ion densities. Thus a 4 MeV α-particle produces 700 times more ionizations per given length than an electron of equal energy.

Every time an ion or excited molecule is produced the energy of the particle is reduced. Instead of ion density it is more precise to speak of *rate of loss of energy* (abbreviated to RLE) especially when we are considering the effect of radiations in liquids and solids where it is not possible to measure the number of ions produced by direct experiment. In gases the Wilson cloud chamber and ionization chamber (see p. 20) enable us to determine the ion density along the tracks of the different particles; no comparable technique exists for making these measurements in liquids or solids. It is often assumed that the number of ions formed is the same in the same *mass* or weight of material. In other words the same number of ions is formed along a 1 cm. track in liquid water as in 1,200 cm. of water vapour. In this way ion densities determined in gases have been used to calculate the number of ionizations produced in tissue, bone, and the like.*

By direct experiment it has been established that every time an ion pair is formed in air by a fast-moving electron this loses on an average about 34 eV of energy. For the heavier particles such as protons the value is 35 eV. This energy is not used up entirely in forming the ion pair, but also produces the excited molecules which are also formed, but whose number it has not so far proved possible to determine by direct experiment. The energy of 34 eV (or 35 eV) is used to produce one ion pair and excite an unknown number of molecules, probably somewhere between two and five. Consequently when an electron produces 10 ion pairs per 1 mm. track it loses 340 eV per mm. in that medium (i.e. the RLE per mm. in that medium is 340 eV).

The rate of loss of energy (RLE) depends on the magnitude of the charge and the velocity of the ionizing particle. It increases as the square of the charge and decreases as the square of the velocity. Thus a proton and an electron moving at the same speed will produce initially the same ionization density, while that of an α-particle will be considerably greater because of its double charge. There is

* There is direct experimental evidence for the postulate that the same amount of energy is lost in an ounce of water vapour which occupies a volume of six gallons as in an ounce of liquid water when these are exposed to the same intensity of radiation. In other words the RLE is proportional to the density of the material. This does not, however, necessarily mean that the ion density is also proportional to the density of the irradiated material, since it is quite possible that the energy needed to form an ion pair is not the same in a gas as it is in a solid or liquid. Neither theory nor experiment can give us any guide. To summarize: while the RLE is proportional to the density of the material, the number of ions formed per unit length – the ion density – may not be so, but in the absence of any evidence to the contrary it is usually assumed to be.

however an important distinction between electrons and protons moving at the same speed; the latter because of their much greater mass have a much greater range. Dr L. H. Gray has likened the behaviour of an electron and a proton to that of a ping-pong ball and a marble of the same size. Moving at the same speed both will initially push the same amount of air out of their path (in this comparison this is equivalent to producing the same number of ionizations). The ping-pong ball, however, will quickly be brought to rest, and during the course of its shorter journey will have displaced much less air than the marble.

In this discussion the behaviour of particles with the same *velocity* has been compared, but to achieve this same velocity the heavier particles require much more energy. When the velocities are considerably less than that of light the energy required to propel the different particles at the same speed is simply proportional to their masses. Thus a proton with energy 1·8 MeV has the same velocity as a 1 keV electron, since the ratio of their masses is 1800 : 1; similarly an α-particle of mass 4 requires four times the energy to move at the same velocity as a proton. As already mentioned, because an α-particle has a charge of 2 its RLE is four times that of a proton of similar speed. As the particles get more energetic this simple relationship between energy, velocity, and mass no longer applies exactly, because of relativistic effects. Thus the velocity of a 100 keV electron as produced in conventional X-ray therapy sets is already attained by a 100 MeV proton. The important point, however, is that when comparing α-particles and protons with electrons of *equal energy*, the former are much more densely ionizing. In radiobiological experiments, as well as in the treatment of cancer, electrons with an energy between 50 keV and 4 MeV are usually used, since these can be produced by γ-rays or in X-ray sets of the types available for therapy. The α-particles used were usually obtained from radon or polonium with energies of approximately 5 MeV. The protons were released by neutrons (see p. 34) or generated in linear accelerators and van de Graaf machines (see Plate

14) with energies of the order of a few MeV. The RLE of electrons of 50 kV is less than one-tenth of that of 5 MeV protons and less than one-hundredth of that of 5 MeV α-particles. For this reason it has become customary to refer to the heavy particles as densely ionizing and to electrons as sparsely ionizing radiations. Whenever α-rays and protons are referred to without an energy being specified it is implied that this is of the order of a few MeV.

As the ionizing particle travels through matter it loses energy and its velocity becomes less until it is too low to produce further ionizations and is essentially brought to rest (i.e., reduced to the same speed as the molecules around it). At the same time as it slows down its RLE increases and the ionizing density therefore increases progressively towards the end of the track. For example a 1 MeV electron will at the beginning of its track lose about 200 eV/μ in water or tissue,* but at the very end of its track its RLE will be about 300 times this value (i.e. nearly as great as that of an α-particle at the beginning of its track). The densely ionizing tail of electrons is extremely short and for the greater part of its track the RLE of a fast electron is low. This is shown diagrammatically in Fig. 4. As we shall see, this densely ionizing tail of a fast electron, although it represents only a small fraction of the total amount of energy dissipated, may be very important biologically. The range, or length of track, of an ionizing particle depends mainly on the density of the material through which it is travelling and only to a small extent on its chemical composition. Since the rate of loss of energy is proportional to the density for a given material (see p. 14) the range must be inversely proportional to density. Thus if the track length of a 50 keV electron in water is 42μ the range in water vapour under normal pressures will be 50,000μ (or 5 cm.) since the ratio of the densities of water to water vapour is 1200 : 1. Fig. 5 shows the relationship between energy and range in

* The micron (μ) is a unit of length equal to 0·001 mm.; i.e. 1/25,000 inch. It is a convenient measure for microscopic dimensions since it is a length which can be revealed by the ordinary optical microscope.

water for different particles.* Water is chosen for all these examples since it approximates to the properties of living tissue, which is only slightly more dense.

The stopping power of different chemical materials is not quite the same. Essentially this stopping power depends on

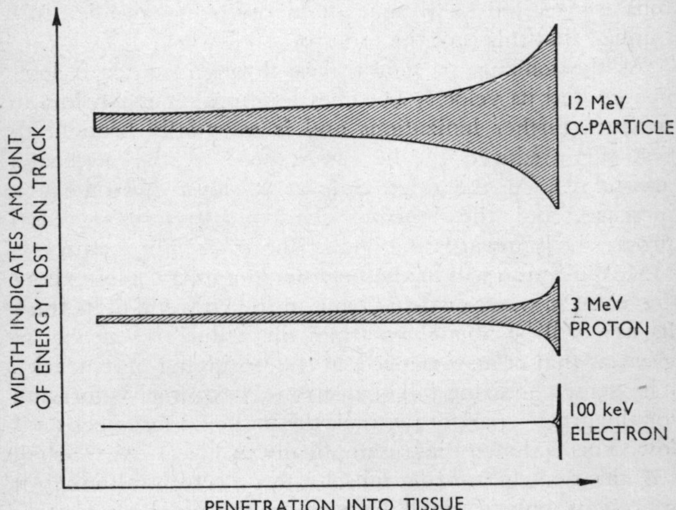

Fig. 4 – Loss of energy of different particles along their track. All three particles have the same range (140μ in tissue); the amount of energy they lose is represented by the width of the track. The electron has only an extremely short 'tail' in which it loses much energy. The 'tail' from the α-particle and proton is much longer.

the total number of electrons in a given volume of the material. The number of electrons per atom is of course the same as the atomic number of the element (i.e. the number of orbital electrons which balance the positive nuclear

* If the different particles are compared at equal velocities instead of energies, the range of α-particles will be approximately equal to that of protons and more than 1,000 times greater than that of electrons (cf., ping-pong ball and marble analogy on p. 24).

charge; see p. 3). Thus the number of electrons in 1 g. of air is $3{\cdot}01 \times 10^{23}$, in 1 g. of water $3{\cdot}34 \times 10^{23}$, and in 1 g. of iron $2{\cdot}80 \times 10^{23}$. Consequently the difference in stopping power on weight basis between these different materials is not very great. But since iron is ten times as dense as water and 12,000 times as dense as air the length of the tracks or the range will be proportionally different.

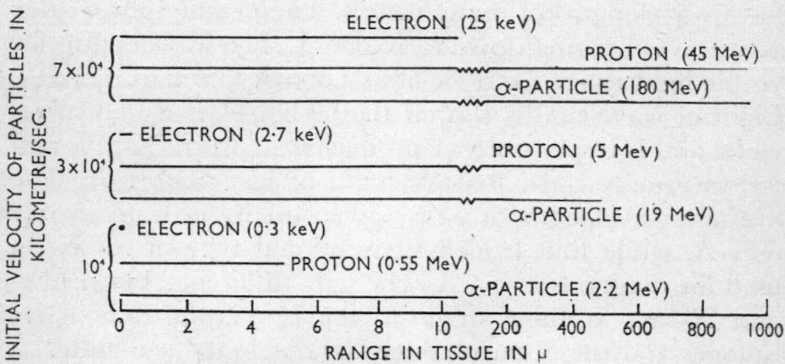

Fig. 5 – Relationship between velocity and range in tissue for different particles.

Thus a 1 MeV electron will be stopped completely by 1 cm. of water or 0·1 cm. of iron.

Penetration. The α- and β-rays given off by radioactive isotopes seldom exceed a few MeV, and can therefore not penetrate very deeply into the body. Exposure to such radiations is therefore only likely to produce skin burns which are usually not serious except when the doses are very high. These radiations become dangerous if the radioactive material is ingested or inhaled. Some of the isotopes are retained for long periods in the body – sometimes permanently – when the α- or β-radiations can be extremely dangerous, since vital organs are exposed and a cancer hazard is set up (see p. 150). In the following section we shall consider other radiations, X-rays, γ-rays, and neutrons which are much more penetrating. On exposure to these radiations the affected parts are not confined to the skin, but every part of the body will be irradiated. Under these conditions much smaller doses of radiation are dangerous.

X-RAYS AND γ-RAYS

These radiations are light waves of very short wavelengths.* They are waves of the same type as radio-waves but these have wavelengths of many metres. Then come infra-red or heat waves ranging down to 10,000 Å. The wavelengths for visible light range from violet at 4,000 Å to red at 9,000 Å. Light of wavelengths shorter than 4,000 Å is called ultra-violet and is responsible for producing sunburn. X-rays and γ-rays usually have a wavelength of less than 1 Å. The average wavelength of γ-rays given off by radium is only 0·01 Å, while that from a conventional type of X-ray set used for diagnosis is 0·5 Å. The only difference between γ- and X-rays is their origin – the one from radioactive isotopes and the other produced by machines (see Plates 14 and 15). In the present discussion X-rays only will be referred to, but all the statements will apply equally to γ-rays.

Although the physical nature of all the radiations, ranging from wireless waves to X-rays, is the same (i.e. they are all electromagnetic radiations), the effects they produce are entirely different. All the radiations give up energy to the molecules through which they pass in packets known as quanta. The shorter the wavelength the more energy-rich are the quanta. The relationship is given by energy of

$$\text{quanta in eV} = \frac{12{,}400}{\text{wavelength in Å}}$$

The energy of X-ray quanta is very high; much more than enough to eject an electron from an atom and produce an ion. Hence they are ionizing radiations like α- and β-rays. The quanta from ultra-violet light are energetic

* Wavelength is measured in an extremely small unit of length, called the Ångström (abbreviated to Å) after a famous Swedish scientist; 1 cm. = 10^8 Å or 1 μ = 10^4 Å (i.e. 10,000 Å = 1μ) or 254,000,000 Å = 1 inch.

enough to excite atoms by changing the arrangement of the electrons in their orbits, but in general they have not enough energy to eject an electron to produce an ion. Quanta of visible light can only excite certain molecules (i.e. those that appear coloured), while the energy from infra-red light is used to vibrate the atoms in a molecule relative to one another, and with few exceptions this energy is directly converted to heat. When we refer to a 100 kV X-ray we mean X-rays having quanta of 100 keV energy. Using the above formula it can be seen that such X-rays have a wavelength of 0·124 Å. X-rays generated with a voltage of 100 kV (i.e. 100,000 V) contain a mixture of radiations with quanta ranging from the maximum possible of 100 keV to very low values. The wavelength of γ-rays and consequently their quantum energy are not nearly so widely spread. It is possible to obtain X-rays of low energy which contain only one wavelength; these are referred to as *soft* X-rays, since they do not penetrate far. The energetic or *hard* X-rays used for biological experiments and the treatment of cancer always contain a wide range of wavelengths.

Release of electrons. When a material is irradiated with X-rays, quanta will be absorbed at random within it and bring about the release of electrons with different energies ranging from that of the quantum down to very low values.* The calculation to determine the number of electrons of each energy is very complex, since there are three quite distinct physical processes by which a quantum of high energy can release a high-energy electron from an atom. The relative frequency of these processes varies with the

* With relatively soft or low voltage X-rays (i.e. up to about 20 keV) the average energy of the electrons released is close to that of the quanta. As the energy of the X-ray quantum rises from 20 keV to 200 keV the average energy of the electrons released increases much more slowly from 15 to 45 keV. For quanta greater than 200 keV the average energy of the electrons increases more rapidly again and for X-rays of 700 keV and upwards it is roughly half the quantum energy. These figures were calculated for water and apply equally to tissue, but will be different for other materials, for example metals.

energy of the X-rays. For our present subject it is not necessary to deal with this problem, and the situation can be summarized as follows: X-rays will release electrons of different energies although none can exceed the quantum energy. The *average* energy of the electrons released for the X-rays and γ-rays most widely employed for therapy and biological experiment lies between one-third and a half of the quantum energy.

Once the X-rays have been converted into electrons, these will behave in just the same way as β-rays. That is, the electrons which have been released will travel through the material and ionize and excite the molecules along their path, and they will have a definite range or track length.

To summarize: X-rays and γ-rays merely act as a means of releasing energetic electrons within the material which is being irradiated. Essentially all the chemical effects are produced by these electrons, since the number of atoms involved in the interaction with the X-ray quanta is minute compared with the number of ionizations produced by the ejected electrons. The following calculation will make this clear. On irradiating water with X-rays having an average wavelength of 0·05 Å (i.e. average energy of quanta = 250 keV) electrons with a mean energy of 60 keV are obtained. Such an electron will ionize approximately 2,000 water molecules, since the energy necessary to form an ion pair in water is about 35 eV (see p. 23). On the average, therefore, one molecule of water is ionized by the direct absorption of the X-ray quantum for every 2,000 water molecules ionized by the electron produced as the result.

There is, however, a very great difference in the distribution of the electron tracks within a material when this is irradiated with X-rays from when it is irradiated with β-rays. This point is illustrated diagrammatically in Fig. 6. If for example a volume of water is exposed to 60 keV β-rays, these begin to ionize the water as soon as they enter its surface, and the ionization will not extend beyond 60μ (i.e. 0·006 cm.) which is the range for electrons of this energy. The X-rays on the other hand are absorbed to a much smaller extent, and can penetrate many centimetres of water or tissue (see next section). As X-rays pass through water an occasional quantum of energy will be absorbed and give rise to a typical β-ray track. A cloud chamber picture showing this random production of β-ray tracks is shown on Plate 2a.

The penetration of X-rays. As X-rays pass through a material they gradually become less intense as more and

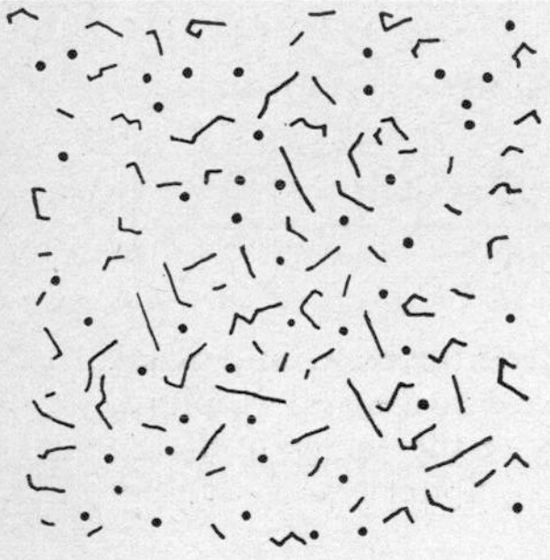

Electron tracks in tissue irradiated with 1 MeV X-rays.

Distribution of tracks in tissue irradiated with 1 MeV electrons.

Fig. 6 – The difference between an irradiation with X- or γ-rays and with electrons (β-rays). 1 MeV X- or γ-rays release electrons ranging in energy from zero to 1 MeV throughout the material and there is little difference between the dose received at the surface and the dose much deeper in. 1 MeV β-rays can only penetrate about $\frac{1}{4}$ in. into tissue, after which nothing is irradiated.

more quanta are absorbed. The intensity of the radiation therefore falls off progressively as it penetrates inside the object being irradiated, and the number of electrons released decreases with penetration. This gradual attenuation is quite different from the dose distribution produced by particulate radiation (e.g. β-rays). The electron enters the water, and its energy deposition is at a minimum on entrance and reaches a maximum at the end of its track. The material beyond its range is not irradiated at all.

X-rays like other light waves are absorbed; the amount of energy deposited becomes less and less as it penetrates, but there is no sharp cut-off as in the case of particulate radiation (see Fig. 7).

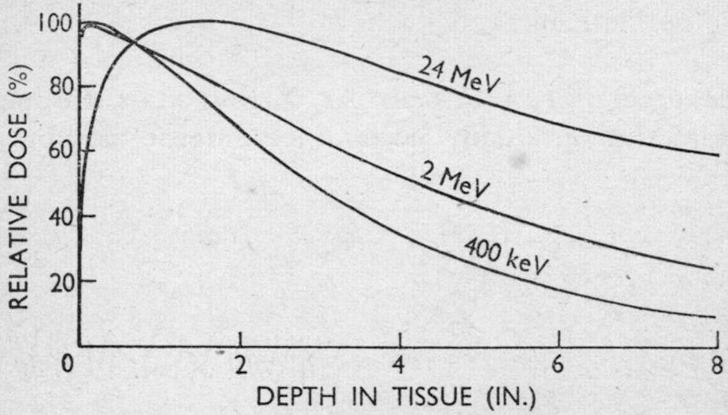

Fig. 7 – Penetration of X-rays of different energies into tissue. It can be seen that for the same surface dose the dose within the irradiated material is greater the higher the energy of the X-rays. This explains why high voltage equipment is so useful for the treatment of deep-seated tumours.

The most important factor to note is that for comparable energies X-rays penetrate much deeper than electrons. Thus a source of 60 keV electrons will be screened completely by a layer of water less than 0·01 cm. (i.e. 1/254 in.) thick, and no radiation whatever will penetrate. The thickness of an iron sheet to provide complete screening need only be one tenth of that of the water layer, since the density of iron is ten times that of water. It is impossible to screen X-rays off absolutely, since their intensity falls slowly with absorption. Thus 250 kV X-rays which give rise to electrons with an average energy of 60 keV will be reduced in intensity to one half after passing through 6 cm. (or more than 2 in.) of water. A further 6 cm. will be needed to reduce the intensity to one quarter, and 18 cm. in all to reduce it to one eighth. For more energetic radiations such as the 2 MeV γ-rays given off by radium the thicknesses needed to produce comparable reductions in intensity will be nearly three times that needed with 0·05 Å X-rays. These figures illustrate the difficulty of protection by screening against high energy X- or γ-rays. With β- and α-rays this problem is relatively simple, and the chief hazard is the eating or breathing in of radioactive material. The absorption of X-rays is directly proportional to the density of the matter through which it passes in exactly the same way as is the stopping power for particulate radiations. For example if 6 cm. of water reduce the X-ray intensity by half, 7,200 cm. of water vapour at ordinary pressure will be necessary for a comparable effect, since its density is only 1/1,200 that of water. When comparing materials of different chemical composition the absorption of X-rays follows the density approximately,* although this relationship does not hold as precisely as for the particulate radiations (see p. 26). The reason for the deviation is that the conversion of the energy from quanta to electrons is rather complex and can involve three different mechanisms, but these deviations need not concern us. Because the absorption of X-rays depends on the density, lead, which is very heavy, is used for screening against these radiations. One inch of lead will give more protection than 1 ft. of water.

The inverse square law. Although the absorption of X-rays by air is extremely small, there is a very marked reduction in dose by increasing the distance between the object irradiated and the radiation source. The reason for this is quite obvious, and is one of everyday experience. We all know that the intensity of illumination from an electric lamp is greater the closer we sit to it. X- and γ-rays are usually given off from a small source such as an ampoule of radium or through the window of a generating tube. As the beam leaves the source it diverges, and, neglecting absorption in the air, the same intensity of X-rays is spread out over a

* The use of X-rays for diagnostic radiography depends on the fact that denser materials such as bones absorb X-rays more than do less dense materials, such as the tissue surrounding the bones. Hence the photographic plate is less blackened in the path of bones.

greater area the further removed it is from the source (see Fig. 8). Simple geometrical considerations show that the intensity falls off as the square of the distance. If in arbitrary units the intensity is 1 at a distance of 1 ft. it will be $\frac{1}{4}$ at 2 ft.

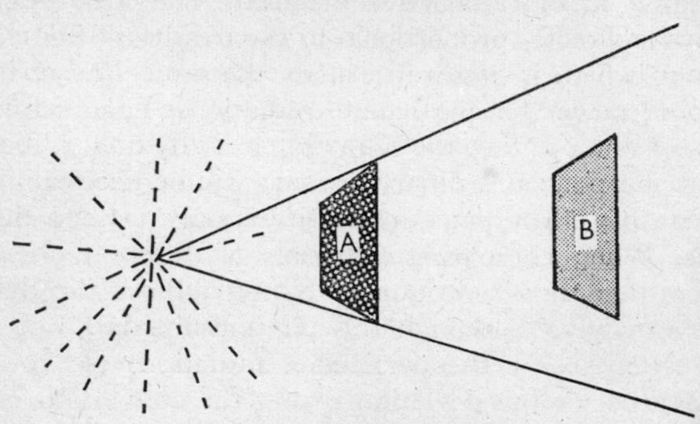

Fig. 8 – Radiation source sends out both rays and particles in all directions. At point A a material receives four times the dose which it would receive at B which is twice the distance away.

and 1/100 at 10 ft. In practice, distance, as the result of the inverse square law, will bring about much greater attenuation of high energy X- and γ-rays than will absorption, except when very dense materials such as lead are used for screening.

NEUTRONS

The effects which occur when a material is exposed to neutrons are much more complex than for the other particulate radiations. The neutrons, being uncharged particles, do not attack or repel the electrons surrounding the atomic nuclei, and therefore cannot produce ions or excited molecules directly. The only process by which a neutron can interact with matter is by direct collision with a nucleus. If the neutron is slow (i.e. does not have much energy) it may be captured by the nucleus to produce an atomic transmutation, and we have already considered this reaction in connexion with the preparation of radioactive isotopes (see p. 12). A much more important process from our point of view is the expulsion of a proton from the nucleus with which the neutron collides. This process occurs readily with so-called fast neutrons having energies of the order of 1 MeV or more, and gives protons of the same order of energy. The projected protons bring about ionization in the way already considered (see p. 22) and have a definite range. The nuclear change leading to the ejection of the proton plays no part in bringing about the biological changes observed after irradiation with neutrons, because the number of atoms transmuted is negligible compared with the number ionized by protons. For example when a neutron ejects a proton with an energy of 1 MeV one atom is changed, while approximately 30,000 will be ionized, and many more excited along the proton track. Plate 2b shows a cloud chamber picture of the track of the protons ejected by a beam of neutrons.

The range of neutrons is very much greater than that of the electrically charged particles, because the nuclei occupy only a minute fraction of the volume of an atom. A neutron can therefore travel long distances before colliding with a nucleus which lies in its path and ejecting a proton. The general effect is rather similar to that brought about by X-rays when short tracks of electrons are produced randomly in the irradiated material. The important difference between neutrons and X-rays is that the former eject particles giving a high rate of loss of energy, while X-rays give rise to electrons of low RLE. Fast neutrons can be used to produce densely ionizing radiation, deep within the irradiated material, which would be inaccessible to heavy particles such as protons which produce the densely ionizing tracks directly.

Shielding against neutrons. The stopping power of a material against fast neutrons depends entirely on the number of nuclei in the path and not on the size of the nuclei or the number of electrons surrounding them. The nucleus of a hydrogen atom has the same chance of stopping a neutron as a nucleus of lead weighing 200 times as much.* Since one gram of water contains thirty times as many atomic nuclei as one gram of lead, it will stop neutrons correspondingly better. For this reason a layer of water will stop neutrons better than an equally thick layer of lead, while for X-rays the latter will be twelve times as effective. The problem of shielding against neutrons is therefore extremely difficult in practice, since dense materials are relatively so ineffective. Consider an X-ray and a neutron source, both of which may be satisfactorily shielded by 3 ft. of concrete. In the case of X-rays similar protection can be obtained with 8 in. of lead, while for neutrons this would be completely insufficient. For these and other reasons fast neutrons represent the most dangerous of all the atomic radiations.

THE 'CURIE' AND THE 'ROENTGEN'

The radiation dose given off by an X-ray machine or by isotopes is usually measured by determining the number of ions produced in a volume of gas. Since these carry an electric charge there are a number of extremely delicate methods by which they can be detected. The widely used Geiger counter consists essentially of a wire stretched inside a cylindrical tube in which electrical conditions are so arranged that an electric current can pass between the wire and the tube only when there are ions in the gas. Consequently when an ionizing particle passes through the tube an electric signal is given out. In this way the number of ionizing particles given off by a radioactive source can be accurately counted. This is called the activity of the material. It is measured in a unit called the 'curie' after the discoverer of radium. The curie is that amount of material in which $3{\cdot}4 \times 10^{10}$ atoms disintegrate per second. The

* For charged particles the stopping power depends on the number of electrons present; consequently the stopping power of a lead atom with eighty-two electrons is eighty-two times as great as that of a hydrogen atom with one electron.

activity of one gram of radium together with its decay products is equal to one curie. Every time an atom disintegrates a β- or α-ray is given off together with a certain amount of γ-radiation.

The activity in curies can tell us nothing about the dose of radiation given off by the radioactive material, since the curie measures only the number of ionizing particles emitted independent of their energy or range. If for example we put next to the skin one curie of radioactive cobalt, ^{60}Co, which gives off energetic γ-rays, the dose received on the surface will be 1/5,000 part of the dose received from one curie of polonium which gives off α-particles. On the other hand the γ-rays from the curie of ^{60}Co will penetrate deeply, while the α-rays will not affect anything which lies more than 2/1,000 in. below the surface of the skin.

The best way of defining the dose of radiation which an irradiated material has received is in terms of energy. We have seen that on exposure to ionizing radiation electrons or other subatomic particles moving at great speed lose energy to the surrounding molecules. The amount of energy gained by the irradiated substance is clearly the important factor and will determine the biological changes produced.* The most widely used unit for measuring X-ray and γ-ray dosage is the *roentgen* – named after the discoverer of X-rays. It is defined as the dose of radiation which produces $2{\cdot}1 \times 10^9$ ion pairs in a volume of one cubic centimetre of air. Although this does not appear to be an energy unit it can readily be converted into one, since 34 eV of energy are transferred to the gas every time an ion pair is formed – part being used to form the ion pair and part to excite other molecules. We can therefore say that exposure

* In very radiation-resistant materials (i.e. in substances whose chemical structure is not changed by irradiation) all this energy will appear as heat. In other cases the ions and excited molecules will not return unchanged to their original constitution but become chemically altered. In this case very little of the energy will appear as heat. As far as the measurement of dose is concerned the subsequent fate of the energy deposited within the irradiated material is not considered.

of water or tissue to 1 roentgen (abbreviated to r) results in an uptake of almost 100 ergs per gram of water or tissue irradiated. This is a minute amount of energy when one considers that 42 million ergs are required to raise the temperature of one gram of water by one degree Centigrade.* The remarkable property of ionizing radiation is that the small amount of energy represented by a few hundred roentgens can kill a man.

The dose given off by an X- or γ-ray source is usually measured in an ionization chamber in which the ions of opposite sign are attracted towards two plates charged respectively positive and negative. The electric current flowing in this chamber is a direct measure of the number of ions produced. For technical reasons the roentgen cannot be applied to the dose of radiation given off by α- and β-rays and by neutrons. For these a somewhat differently defined unit has been used, known as the *rep* (roentgen equivalent physical). As radiations of higher and higher energy are being produced and used in radiation therapy and research into radiobiology, the roentgen and rep, defined in terms of the number of ionizations produced in a gas, have become increasingly difficult to use in practice. A new unit has therefore been introduced known as the *rad* and defined directly in terms of energy absorption. One rad is the quantity of radiation which will result in an energy absorption of 100 ergs per g. of the irradiated material. Numerically the rad is very similar to the roentgen. Since the rad has only been accepted internationally within the last few years it is not yet widely used, and the roentgen is still the most common unit.

* 1 degree Centigrade = 1·8 degrees Fahrenheit.

CHAPTER 2

THE RESPONSE OF THE CELL

THE basic unit of life is the cell. There is a myriad of simple organisms which are made up of one cell only; these may be very small, such as bacteria, or visible to the naked eye like amoeba, but all the more highly developed animals and plants are made up of a very large number of cells. The basic biological action of radiation must initially involve particular cells. In the body the individual cells form part of a highly complex structure. Just as none of the different organs of the body is capable of independent existence, so neither can the individual cells thrive in isolation. This interdependence is of two kinds; cells of the same type growing together form what is called a colony, and the behaviour of the individual cell is conditioned to varying extents by the group. In more complex organisms the secretions by one cell influence and often determine the behaviour of other cells which may be a considerable distance away. When studying the effect of ionizing radiations on complex organisms it is often extremely difficult to determine whether the observed effect is due to damage in the cells being studied or whether an *effect at a distance* is being observed. That effects of this kind occur was demonstrated by irradiating certain parts of an animal only and finding that unirradiated organs were affected. A further difficulty in the interpretation of results of the irradiation of human beings or experimental mammals is the occurrence of a 'stress reaction'. Whenever the body is exposed to a sudden shock – this may be fright without any physical damage, an accident, an operation, or even exposure to extreme cold – nerves which control the pituitary gland become stimulated and secretion of some hormones, notably those controlling the sex glands, is inhibited while that of others is increased. Irradiation with fairly heavy doses produces a response of this type, and changes in certain organs may in this indirect way bring about changes in different organs.

Two typical examples will illustrate the complexities which arise when the whole body of a mammal is irradiated with a dose of X-rays sufficient to cause severe radiation sickness. After such a dose the content in the liver of an important cellular food, glycogen, is greatly increased. This could be due to direct irradiation damage of the liver cells; on the other hand it could have been the result of an increase in the amount of cortisone secreted. Perhaps the most sensitive physiological change which shows that a mammal has received a relatively small dose of radiation is a fall in the number of lymphocytes, one of the various types of cell in the blood (see p. 93). Isolated lymph glands free from all hormonal influence are very sensitive both to radiation and to cortisone. Is the reduction of the lymphocytes in the blood of an animal due to a radiation effect on the cells themselves or is it the result of stress?

To obtain fundamental information about the biological effect of atomic radiation we must therefore study its effects on isolated cells or cell colonies. A very large amount of information has been obtained by studying unicellular organisms, but it must be remembered that their growth and development takes place in an entirely different way from that of multicellular animals.

GROWTH AND SPECIALIZATION

There is no such thing as a typical cell; all cells have their own individual characteristics and histologists can generally determine from which organ a particular cell is derived. The size of a cell is usually of the order of a hundredth part of a millimetre (i.e. 10μ, see p. 25) and bears no relation to the size of the organ from which it is obtained. In fact, extremely large cells are frequently found in very small animals and factors like this determine the type of animal which is most suitable for any particular experiment. Many cells, particularly those in very simple organisms, are spherical or ellipsoid. The cells of the highly specialized organs in more advanced forms of life are of many shapes; for example, nerve cells send out threadlike feelers which may extend over several feet. In spite of all these diversities a remarkable unity underlies the basic structure of the cell. Plates 3 and 6 show what can be seen of a cell with the optical and the electron microscope. Fig. 9 gives a diagrammatic representation of the components of a cell which is

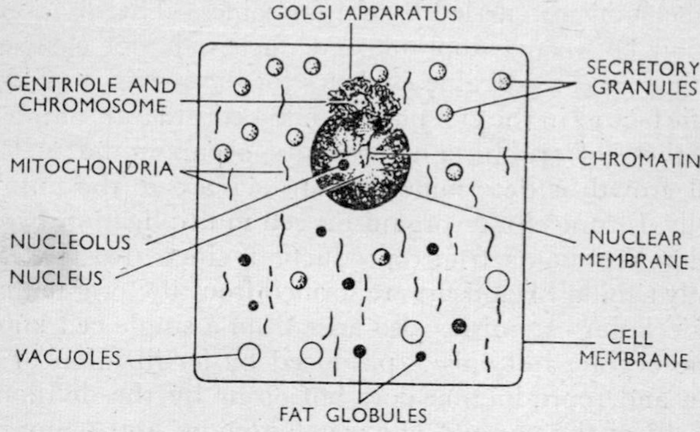

Fig. 9 – Diagrammatic representation of the organization in a cell which can be rendered visible in the optical microscope.

not undergoing division. The round structure near the centre, which is sharply differentiated from the rest of the cell, is the nucleus; the remainder of the cell mass is known as the cytoplasm, and contains a large number of small granules–most of them not visible in the optical microscope. Both the nucleus and the surrounding cytoplasm are vital to life and the duplication of the cell. In a few isolated instances it is possible to remove the nucleus and replace it by another; with a particular species of algae a cell with its nucleus removed continues to grow and assimilates food for a few days. In general, however, any attempt to separate the nucleus from the cytoplasm kills the cell.

A very great deal is known concerning the relative functions of the cytoplasm and the nucleus, and a general pattern is emerging, although a number of key questions remain unanswered. As an extreme over-simplification we may consider the cytoplasm as the factory of the cell in which food is broken down and converted into energy as well as into small molecules which are then used as intermediates in the synthesis of complex molecules needed by the cell either for maintenance or for duplication. The main function of the nucleus is to ensure the exact reproduction of the cell, when it divides, by duplicating the cellular control mechanisms carried by chromosomes. The division of function between cytoplasm and nucleus is not clear-cut, and there is considerable evidence for the presence of some genetic factors in the cytoplasm while a considerable amount of synthesis of structural material also occurs in the nucleus.

All growth is determined by an increase in the number of cells. In unicellular organisms cell multiplication by cell division represents true reproduction, since two new and exactly similar organisms are formed from the original cell. Multicellular organisms also arise from a single cell known as the zygote, but this is produced by fertilization of the ovum and reproduction does not occur by the division of the cells of the parent. The zygote divides and many new cells are produced, but these are not alike; very early in this process different types of cells are produced which later become the specialized cells which make up specific tissues and organs in the animal and plant. In complex organisms cell division is not confined to growth and reproduction, but is necessary for the maintenance of the adult. Damage has to be made good, and many specialized cells, such as those making up the outer layers like skin, or linings of the stomach and intestine as well as the cells which make up the blood, have only a short life and must be replaced continually. In general, once cells have become highly specialized (this is known as differentiation) they no longer reproduce by cell division. It is possible to grow some outside the body, where they can often be made to divide, but they will not do this in their normal environment unless some special circumstances demand it. Two types of highly differentiated cells, those making up muscles and nerves, can never be made to divide, and injury to them cannot be made good by cell division of neighbouring undamaged cells. The replacement of differentiated cells is usually brought about by stimulating some less highly specialized cell to divide, and the daughter cell produced in this way will then differentiate until it has acquired all the special functions and can replace the damaged cell. For example, the cells in the outer layer of skin have to fulfil specialized functions, and while developing the capacity to discharge these duties they have lost the ability to divide. However, some way below the surface there are other types which can divide and whose daughter cells move upwards to replace the cells on the surface.

In general, differentiated cells are much less sensitive to ionizing radiations, which exert their biological effects in animals by changing cells which are dividing or at least are capable of multiplying by division when called upon to do so by some stimulus. However, it would not be wise to stress this generalization since there is no definition for degree of specialization. In the next section the process of division will be described; in its general outline it is common to all cells and represents their most characteristic property. At a well-defined point the cell changes into identical units and thus duplicates itself exactly.

CELL DIVISION

The period between divisions has been given the very misleading name of 'resting stage'. In this period the cell is by no means stagnant and intense synthetic activity takes place; however, in the optical microscope the nucleus undergoes no visible changes, and this gave rise to the name.

Almost all cells will divide when placed in a favourable environment. Unicellular organisms such as bacteria if suspended in a suitable medium will divide until their food becomes exhausted or division is prevented by the accumulation of toxic waste products. Cell division also occurs in growing plants and animals, but all the cells produced are not alike, and some unknown factors determine for example which cell becomes a nerve cell and which forms connective tissue. Multiplication by cell division continues until maturity is reached and the organs and tissues have reached their maximum size. Growth by multiplication then stops, and these cells remain in the 'resting' stage during which they will perform any special function such as secretion of hormones or milk (in the case of the mammary glands). Multiplication of these cells will only recur when initiated by some external stimulus such as injury or a hormonal excretion. These cells are called somatic and may persist during the whole life of the animal. As already mentioned, the fully specialized cells which perform the intricate functions required for nerve and muscle action cannot be made to multiply under any circumstances, and once lost cannot be replaced. Other cells in the adult are continuously replaced; the blood cells are inherently short-lived, and the dead cells are removed mainly by the spleen. The outer layers of skin and cornea and the mucous membranes are also renewed all the time, but the dead cells are taken away by mechanical processes of wear and tear.

After an injury cell division sets in once again until the damage has been repaired. The key problem of cancer research is: what stimuli cause a cell to stop dividing when an organ reaches the correct size, and to repair damage after an injury? Cells from organs which have reached adult size and which will no longer grow within the animal can be transferred and grown in the laboratory under completely artificial conditions. If the medium contains the right food all cells, unless they are very highly differentiated, will immediately multiply in the same way as bacteria; an experiment of this type is known as tissue culture. If the experiment is conducted properly – and high skill and experience are necessary – these cultured cells will continue to grow indefinitely. A possible, though not necessary, conclusion is that cells have an inherent tendency to divide which is held in check in the body of the animal. The time for division varies; for bacteria it may be as little as ten minutes; in mammals it is about forty-five minutes, and increases to several hours in cold-blooded animals and to a day or more in plants.

In the 'resting' stage between divisions the cell is highly active getting ready for its duplication in division. Somatic cells in the body although not preparing for division are nevertheless continually breaking up their structural components and replacing them; they are not static structures, which only show activity if they have any specialized function, such as contraction of muscle cells or production of hormones by cells from the adrenals. In all cells under normal conditions substances are being continually broken down and replaced, and cells are never old in the sense that they are made up of the same substance as when they were formed. In a somatic cell the structure is maintained stationary by an exact balance between synthesis and destruction. When a cell prepares for division there will be a net gain in synthesis during the resting or intermitotic stage.

Even under the microscope somatic cells and cells between division do not appear to be at rest, and this is beautifully revealed by taking a moving film. By projecting this more rapidly (i.e. opposite of slow motion) all motion is accelerated and becomes clearly visible. Successive 'stills' of such films are shown in Plate 4 and from these movements of the little particles in the cytoplasm and of the cell membrane can be seen. When the cell is not dividing only the nucleus appears to be at rest, but even this is merely due to the fact that the activity is not at a level which the microscope can reveal, and synthesis of materials is going on most actively. In fact during division when there is much visible activity in the nucleus chemical changes are at a minimum.

Division. During the process known as mitosis the nucleus duplicates itself; the cytoplasm cleaves into two parts and when it is complete two cells, each identical with the original one, are formed. During mitosis a most wonderful sequence of changes occur in the nucleus, and these are shown in Plates 4 and 5. In the first stage – the prophase – strands appear in the nucleus, and these gradually condense and contract into distinct threads called chromosomes.* As this process develops it becomes apparent that these threads are composed of two filaments, known as chromatids. Simultaneously with the appearance of the chromosomes the nuclear membrane contracts and finally disappears, leaving the chromosomes packed closely together in the cytoplasm. At this time a gel-like structure (known as the spindle and stretching out from the centre) appears in the cytoplasm.

In the next stage – the metaphase – the spindle becomes attached to the chromosomes, which now arrange themselves in an orderly manner in a plane at the centre of the cell. During this process the chromosomes contract and can no longer be seen to be composed of two chromatids. This becomes dramatically apparent at anaphase, when the chromosomes suddenly divide and the spindle pulls the two sets of chromatids to the opposite ends of the cell (i.e. the two chromatids from every chromosome move in opposite directions so that two identical sets are produced). The division is completed in telophase when the cytoplasm cleaves into two approximately equal masses divided by a new cellular membrane; the nuclear membrane reforms, and the chromosomes in the daughter nuclei swell until they can no longer be resolved with the microscope and the nucleus assumes the appearance of the resting cell.

During mitosis our attention has been focused on the precision of the chromosome ballet, and the apparently more random and haphazard behaviour of the cytoplasm can easily be forgotten. Yet the cytoplasmic, just as much as the nuclear, equipment has been duplicated and the granules in the cytoplasm are distributed during telophase between the two daughter cells. At prophase cytoplasmic activity decreases and cells – like those in tissue culture –

* The number of chromosomes per cell varies widely, and depends on the animal or organism from which it is derived; for example, human cells have forty-six chromosomes while those of beans have twelve.

which are irregular in shape become rounded. At telophase the cytoplasm becomes the centre of action and bubbles which rapidly swell and shrink appear on the surface of the cell. This irregular movement finishes soon after the completion of the division and the cell behaves normally.

Meiosis. Normal cell division ensures duplication of identical cells, and the growth of differentiated organs and of unicellular organisms occurs in this way. The reproduction of multicellular organisms is brought about by the

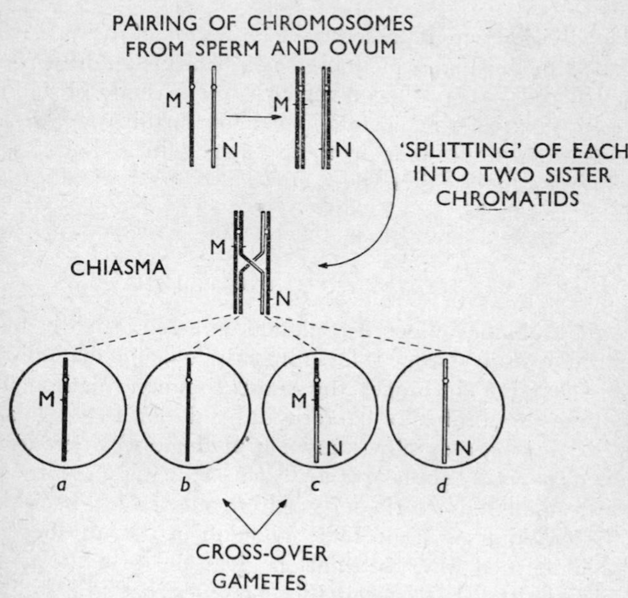

Fig. 10 – *Reductive division:* Each of the chromosomes in the sperm or the ovum is paired to give a fertile egg with twice the number of chromosomes. The behaviour of these paired chromosomes in the subsequent division processes is shown for one set of chromosomes here. The diagram also illustrates how two genes (see Chapter 4) present in two different precursor cells are distributed within the different gametes.

union of sex cells (the egg and the sperm) which have undergone a unique series of cell divisions to ensure the mixing of chromosomes. Since these carry the elements, called genes, which determine inherited characteristics, this exchange of parts of the chromosome is vital to life, since it is the only mechanism whereby the progeny receives characteristics from both parents (see Chapter 4). The sperm and ovum (the gametes) contain only half the normal number of chromosomes and the original number is re-established during their fusion to give the fertilized egg or zygote. The latter grows by cell division and differentiation into a new animal.

The division which precedes the formation of the gametes is called meiosis, in which by a complex mechanism (see Fig. 10) cells are produced which contain single chromosomes instead of the normal pairs. On fertilization these single chromosomes pair up to give a cell with a double set of chromosomes which is exactly reproduced in all subsequent cell divisions.

SENSITIVITY TO RADIATION

The most obvious effect of radiation on a cell is death, but even this drastic change is far from easy to define for individual cells. For instance, the most common method of counting the number of bacteria in a solution is to spread this evenly on a rich jelly (known as plating out) when after a few days visible spots appear, each one being a colony of many millions of bacteria derived from one or a few bacteria in the original solution. The reduction in the number of colonies formed after irradiation gives the proportion of bacteria killed. It is conceivable, however, that the radiation did not 'kill' the cells but merely prevented them from multiplying. A different test, such as measuring the amount of oxygen or food consumed by the bacteria before and after irradiation, might show an entirely different situation; it may happen that these measurements may show little change until many hours after the irradiation. This would mean that the cells were not killed but prevented from dividing. With bacteria and other cells which have only a short life span this difference is probably only of scientific interest, but with cells capable of existing without division this difference may be profound (see, for example, p. 43), and its implication in the treatment of cancer by radiation is discussed on p. 134.

One of the most remarkable features of ionizing radiation is the difference in sensitivity of different organisms. Using death as criterion Table II shows that doses vary from 200 r for mammals to 200,000 r* for some unicellular organisms.

TABLE II

Radiation resistance of different animals and micro-organisms

	Radiation dose necessary to kill (LD50)*
Mammals	200–1,000 r
Goldfish	700 r
Frog	700 r
Tortoise	1,500 r
Newt	3,000 r
Snail	10,000 r
Yeast	30,000 r
Bacterium coli	10,000 r
Fruit-fly (adult) and other insects	60,000 r
Amoeba	100,000 r
Paramecia	300,000 r

* For definition of LD50 see p. 74.

The unit of dose for atomic radiations, the roentgen 'r', is defined on p. 36. The sensitivity of isolated mammalian cells in tissue culture also varies greatly; while lymphocytes may be killed by 300 r some cells from the skin may require 5,000 r. This difference is particularly marked for various blood cells whose sensitivity to radiation may vary over a

* For mammals a time interval (usually thirty days) has to be specified within which death has to occur since even quite small doses of radiation are deleterious and reduce the average life-span (see p. 77).

tenfold range. Nevertheless no mammalian cell has a resistance approaching that of most unicellular organisms. The radiosensitivity of insects is intermediate between that of mammals and unicellular organisms.

No convincing reason has yet been put forward to explain why there are these tremendous variations between different cells in their response to radiation; only when this is known will it become possible to base radiotherapy of cancer or methods of protection against radiation on a reliable foundation. It is a measure of the difficulty and complexity of the subject that not even a tentative answer can be given to the question. Many clues have been found by comparing the effect of radiation on individual cells – the subject of this chapter - with the chemical changes produced, since it is these which initiate the biological damage (see Chapter 8).

RETARDING CELL DIVISION

The most easily detectable change when cells are irradiated with doses insufficient to kill them is a hold-up in cell division for a limited period of time and consequently a retardation of growth. Studies of this type have shown that the sensitivity of the cell varies and depends on the particular stage it has reached in its mitotic cycle when it is irradiated. Mitosis does not stop immediately after irradiation but goes on for some little time, and then comes a period where there is no division. The reason for this delay is that cells which have started division are not particularly sensitive to radiation and the cells most affected are those which are still a little way from division.

When examining a culture of mammalian cells or cells from growing plants a proportion of these can be seen to be undergoing cell division (that is, the chromosomes in the nucleus are clearly visible and somewhere between prophase and telophase). Under laboratory controlled conditions the relative number of dividing and resting cells can be maintained constant and the effect of radiation on this ratio can

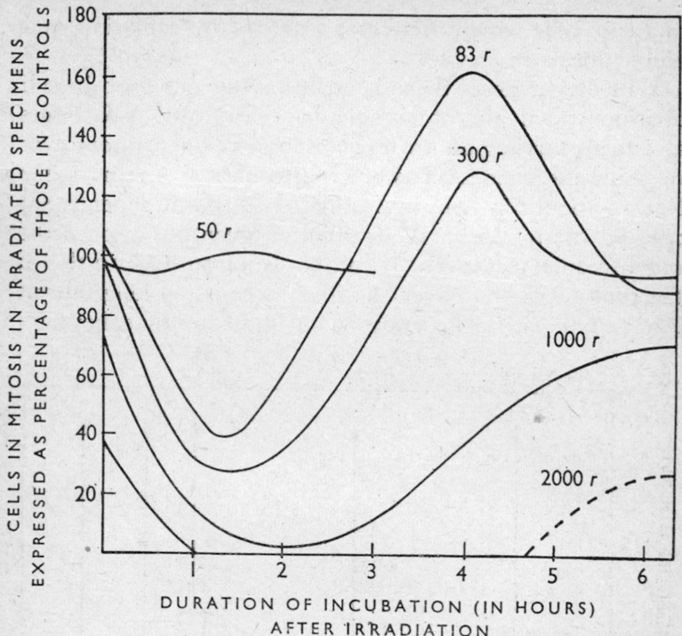

Fig. 11 – Effect of increasing doses of X-rays on the rate of cell division of cells grown in tissue culture (chick fibroblasts). Up to 300 r there is only a temporary depression and after the compensatory wave the culture returns to normal. With 1,000 and 2,000 r, mitosis is completely suppressed for a time and the culture does not recover completely.

be measured. In Fig. 11 the effect of different doses of X-rays on cells in tissue culture is shown; immediately after irradiation with small doses the number of dividing cells is unchanged, but falls and reaches a minimum after one to two hours; thereafter the mitotic activity increases again and there is a compensatory wave of cell division greater than normal after which the culture settles down to normal. The temporary increase in cell division in the second part of the S-curve is not due to any stimulation of cell growth by radiation but is the result of the simultaneous entry into division of the cells which had been arrested, in addition to those cells which were not affected by radiation and divide normally.

With larger doses there is an instantaneous drop in cell division which almost completely ceases after two hours and then starts again an hour or so later but without ever reaching the same level as before irradiation. A remarkable feature about this hold-up in division is that it depends not only on the total dose of irradiation given but also on the rate at which it is given. It can be seen from Fig. 12 that if the time taken to deliver the fixed dose is too long mitosis is not suppressed. This experiment illustrates that there are

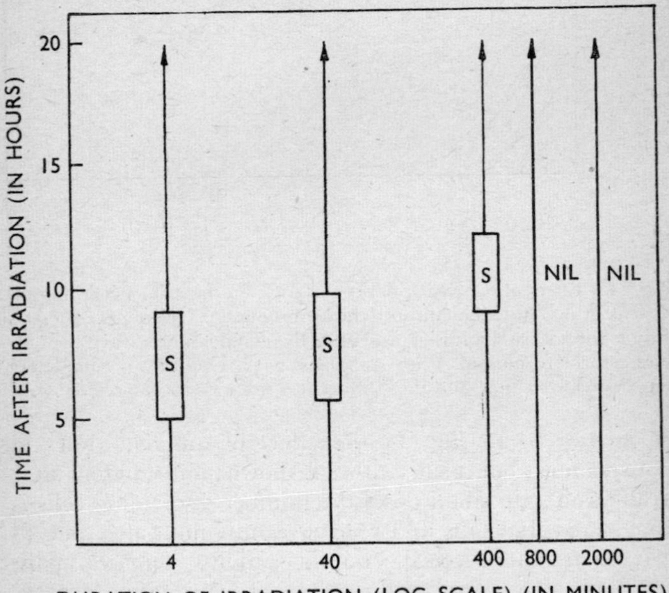

Fig. 12 – Temporary suppression of cell division in pollen grains (*Tradescantia*) by a dose of 200 r of X-rays.

The higher the dose rate (that is the shorter the time of irradiation), the more marked is the effect (S represents period of mitosis suppression). At the lowest dose rates no effect is observed.

ways in which cells can recover from radiation injury: an important factor to which I shall refer again in detail in Chapter 7.

It has been found that if the dose *rate* exceeds a certain value the effectiveness of the radiation in stopping mitosis falls again. In other words there is a dose rate at which for a given dose the mitotic arrest is greatest. This suggests that there is a short period in the mitotic cycle when the cell is most susceptible to damage, and by reducing the time during which the radiation is given beyond a certain value not all the cells will be exposed during their critical stage.

Investigations from many other directions also show that the cell is not equally sensitive to irradiation in all phases of its existence. This becomes clearly apparent when one irradiates cells with different doses of radiation.

As an example,* we may consider mammalian cells in tissue culture: with extremely large X-ray doses, usually more than 100,000 r, all cells are killed immediately the dose has been delivered – the time to do this depends on the efficiency of the generator used. This instantaneous death is due to widespread chemical changes produced by the large amount of radiation, and is of little interest, since it is comparable to hitting cells with a sledge hammer. With doses exceeding 10,000 r all cells will eventually die; some will be killed immediately after irradiation, but some (the proportion depending on the dose) will continue to live and even divide, but degeneration occurs and eventually the culture will die. With doses of the order of 1,000 r, degeneration leading to delayed death occurs only in some of the cells, while others survive. This behaviour is shown in Fig. 11, where the culture settles down after irradiation to a lower level of mitotic rate because some cells have been killed. Since all the cells in the culture are very similar,

* Most cells will show this same type of behaviour, but the dose levels at which the transition takes place from one type of effect to another will vary with the material used. The doses will in general be smaller for plant cells and larger for unicellular organisms than in the example described.

having been derived by mitosis from a few related cells (i.e. not by meiosis, when chromosome exchanges occur), the resistance of some of the cells cannot be attributed to normal biological variation. Cells irradiated while actually in division (i.e. at metaphase, anaphase, or telophase) complete the mitotic cycle with little or no delay and usually survive and successfully undergo further division. Cells irradiated at interphase (i.e. in the resting stage) or in the very first visible stage of division (early prophase) will be affected and will not divide for one hour or more (i.e. mitotic arrest); after the period of mitotic delay is over the cells may again divide normally, although some – the number depends on the dose – will degenerate and show

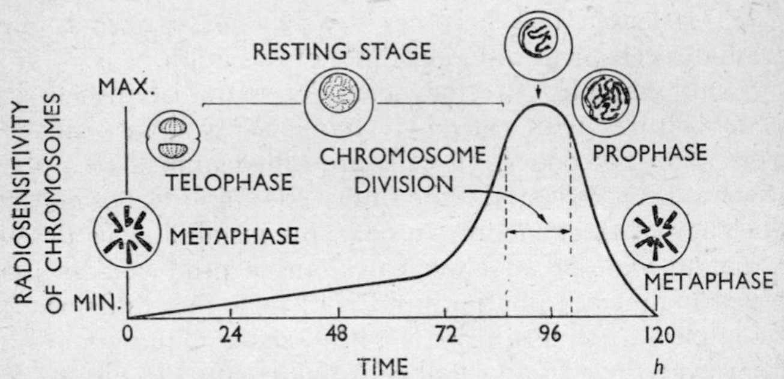

Fig. 13 – Diagram illustrating the change in sensitivity of the chromosomes to radiation during the mitotic cycle.

delayed death. Well-designed experiments indicate that the cell is most sensitive at the very end of the resting stage and the very early part of prophase. This is shown diagrammatically in Fig. 13, which is based on experiments with pollen from the common plant wandering sailor (or *Tradescantia*) a material widely used for this type of experiment.

To summarize: With small doses of irradiation (e.g. 300 r for the system shown in Fig. 11) temporary mitotic arrest is the only immediately observable effect – and after a delay all the cells divide and, apart from a possible genetic effect which would only affect a minute fraction of the cells (see Chapter 4), the culture is then normal and appears to have suffered no permanent harm. The first division after the radiation-induced mitotic delay often shows some abnormalities, the most common being an apparent 'stickiness' of the chromosomes so that the migration of the split chromosomes at anaphase is not quite as clean as usual. Subsequent divisions, however, do not show this and chromosome stickiness is not deleterious to the life of the cell.

As the dose of radiation is increased above that necessary to produce only mitotic arrest some of the cells (the proportion increasing with the dose) which have gone into division after some delay are not normal and will degenerate. The radiation has not killed the cells outright, but has produced some permanent defect which is not repaired and which the cell cannot overcome. This injury, while not preventing one and perhaps even two or three divisions, eventually brings about the death of *all* the cells which were derived from the one which had been initially damaged. The injury which brings about this delayed death is breaking of chromosomes, but this does not occur equally readily at all stages of the mitotic cycle and consequently all cells are not equally affected by a given dose of radiation.

BREAKING CHROMOSOMES

The first changes in irradiated cells visible under the microscope occur in the nucleus, and as the cells degenerate and are approaching death, many other changes, particularly in the shape of the cell membrane, become apparent and have occupied the attention of histologists and anatomists. They are of technical interest and of great importance for following the course of radiation treatment in cancer, but are unlikely to contribute to our understanding of the mechanism of action of radiation on the cell. This interesting topic receives considerable attention in a lucid book written for the non-specialist by one of the pioneers in this field, Dr F. G. Spear (see Bibliography).

Changes in the cell nucleus can be classified as temporary

or permanent; chromosome stickiness is one of the most prominent manifestations of the former type which is believed to be closely related to delay in mitosis. Permanent changes of chromosomes are not repaired and are perpetuated in subsequent divisions and can therefore lead to delayed degeneration and death which is such a characteristic feature of radiation injury. These permanent chromosome changes are usually seen at metaphase or anaphase in the division following the irradiation. Since the cell is most sensitive in the resting stage when the chromosomes are not visible and very insensitive at metaphase and anaphase when chromosomes can be seen very clearly, it must be borne in mind that we do not see what happens to the chromosomes at the time of irradiation. Consequently when it is stated that a certain chromosome change has been observed as a result of irradiation this is not strictly true; the exact statement should be that the effect of the irradiation at the resting stage has given rise to the change seen at metaphase. This point is not as pedantic as it might appear, but has an important bearing on the interpretation of the results.

The usual explanation of permanent chromosome changes is that they are the result of breaks in the chromosomes produced by irradiation. The broken ends are believed to have the ability to re-join under certain conditions, and when they fuse together again in exactly the same way as before irradiation, the damage is completely restored and no permanent injury has occurred. Different types of reunions can, however, occur to give new chromosome configurations different from those originally present, and these give rise to a large number of different abnormalities which can be seen under the microscope. A proportion of the breaks remain open and these are seen as broken chromosomes. On this hypothesis the exact sequence of events depends on whether the break has occurred before the chromosome has split to give two chromatids, a process of splitting which probably occurs at the end of resting stage or very early in prophase; that is at a time when the cell is most sensitive. The normal process may be represented as follows:

(A) SPLIT

CHROMOSOME CHROMATIDS

Breakage can then be pictured

(B) X-RAY SPLIT

X-ray produces breaks in chromosomes which are followed by splitting to give two broken chromatids. These may rejoin to give the following abnormal structures which are seen at metaphase or anaphase

(C) OR

If X-rays act after the split only one chromatid is broken.

(D) X-RAY

When breaks are formed in chromosomes close together many types of reunions giving rise to different configurations are possible;

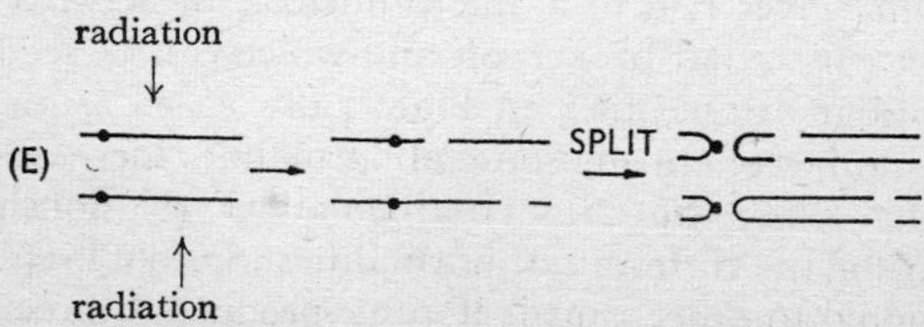

giving on reunion for example

which can be observed at metaphase in irradiated cells. A few typical chromosome breaks are shown in Plate 7a. It must be stressed again that the only change actually observed is the final metaphase abnormality and that the earlier stages are inferred. If the reunion occurs before the chromosomes split, structures of the following type are formed.

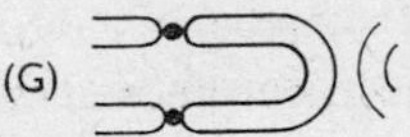

Now, when the cell enters anaphase the two pairs of each chromosome move apart into opposite sides of the cell. When they are joined in this way this process is interfered with and a bridge is formed between the two sets of chromosomes

i.e. at anaphase the whole cell looks like this

(compare Plate 7a) and this will obviously greatly hinder the completion of cell division. Such a cell when it succeeds in dividing gives rise to a micro-nucleus formed from the fragment which had broken off and which can be seen next to the bridge at anaphase in Plate 7a.

The number of chromosome abnormalities increases with increasing dose, but the mathematical relationship is different for the different abnormalities. Simple breaks are proportional to dose; that is if 100 r produces 6 breaks per hundred cells then 200 r will produce 12 breaks. More complicated abnormalities such as those obtained by chromatid exchange occur less frequently, but increase rapidly with dose; if 100 r gives 1 chromatid exchange, 200 r will produce between 3 and 4. The number of chromosome abnormalities produced also depends on dose rate, although the effect is not so marked as for mitosis suppression, which does not occur at all at very low dose rates (see Fig. 12).

Chromosome breaks occur at all dose rates, but the numbers seen for a certain dose increase with an increase in the rate at which it is delivered. In *Tradescantia* pollen 200 r given at the rate of 50 r/min. (i.e. in 4 minutes) is twice as effective as 200 r given at 0·5 r/min. (i.e. in 400 minutes). This dose rate dependence fits in very well with the mechanism just described, since the chance of a chromosome abnormality being produced depends on the presence of two breaks in close proximity at the same time. The probability of this occurring will be greater at high dose rates than at low, since the breaks are assumed to stay open for only a few minutes. Unless another break is produced close by within this period the first will reconstitute and no injury will be seen. However, most biological effects of radiation are dependent on dose rate, because recovery processes in general run parallel with the development of the injury (see Chapter 7) and this may also be the explanation in the case of chromosome breaks, rather than the mechanical interpretation just given.

A mathematical theory based on the breakage and reunion hypothesis above predicts accurately the observed dependence of the effects on total dose and dose rate. This quantitative agreement between theory and experiment provides some of the best evidence for the correctness of the assumptions, although it must be stressed that it does not by any means constitute proof. A fair statement of the position is probably that the extensive experimental data on the effect of radiation on chromosomes can be satisfactorily explained by assuming that chromosomes are broken both before and after they have split into chromatids, and that the broken ends may restitute in the original way, remain open to give breaks, or reunite in new combinations to give many different kinds of abnormality.

Before considering the role of chromosome breakage in relation to the killing of cells by radiation the limited and contradictory data on the chemical mechanism by which chromosome breaks are produced will be considered, since this is necessary before an assessment of the role of chromosome breaks in radiation injury can be made.

How are chromosomes broken? There are two extreme views which can be adopted. A purely mechanical interpretation would be to consider the breaking of chromosomes as like the snapping of a cable by a rifle bullet; an ionizing particle (such as an electron ejected by X-rays or a proton or α-particle) breaks the thread it hits. A quite opposite view is to consider that the ionizing radiations interfere with the ability of the cell to make chromosome material; this is a process which occurs in the resting stage when the cell is most sensitive to radiation. The chromosome break is then a visible manifestation of the interruption in synthesis.* At the outset it must be stated that neither of these hypotheses can be correct and that a theory will have to be evolved which incorporates features of both.

There are two important experimental facts which point in opposite directions and which will have to be reconciled before the answer is found. Densely ionizing radiations such as α-particles or protons are much more effective than fast electrons either from β-rays or ejected within the irradiated material by X- or γ-rays. The comparison is, of course, made when equal amounts of energy have been deposited. An α-particle crossing a cell will leave behind much more energy than an electron because the former ionizes many

* Chromosomes are made up of very large molecules known as nucleoproteins, the exact chemical structure of which is not yet known. However, much work is being done to determine the effect of irradiation on nucleoproteins which have been extracted from the cell and this will be referred to in Chapter 10.

more atoms along the track than the electron. When a cell has received an equal dose of X- and α-rays there will be the same amount of energy deposited (or in other words nearly the same number of atoms ionized), but the distribution of the energy deposition will be quite different. This is shown diagrammatically in Fig. 14, which is not to scale;

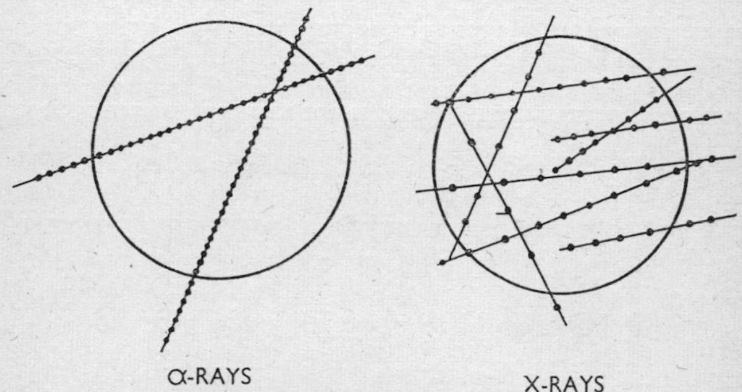

Fig. 14 – Diagrammatic representation showing the difference in the distribution of the ionization when a cell is irradiated with equal doses (i.e. equal amounts of energy) of α-rays and X-rays. (Not to scale.)

in this illustration bombardment with α-particles results in densely ionizing tracks across the cell; irradiation with X-rays produces electrons throughout the material; some of them start within the cell, others were released outside, but enter the cell. The rate of loss of energy along the electron tracks is small. On the mechanical theory the greater effectiveness of densely ionizing radiations is readily understood, since to break an existing structure a minimum amount of energy will be necessary.

The brilliant English physicist Douglas Lea analysed the data existing up to the time of his death in 1947 and concluded that an ionizing particle can only break a chromosome if in the part of the track which crosses it 700 eV of energy are deposited (this is believed to be equivalent to twenty ionizations). Along its track the ionization density is at least high enough for twenty ionizations to occur in the width of the chromosomes. In other words a chromosome is only broken if the ionizing particle which crosses it loses 700 eV in the process. Fig. 15 shows that α-particles and

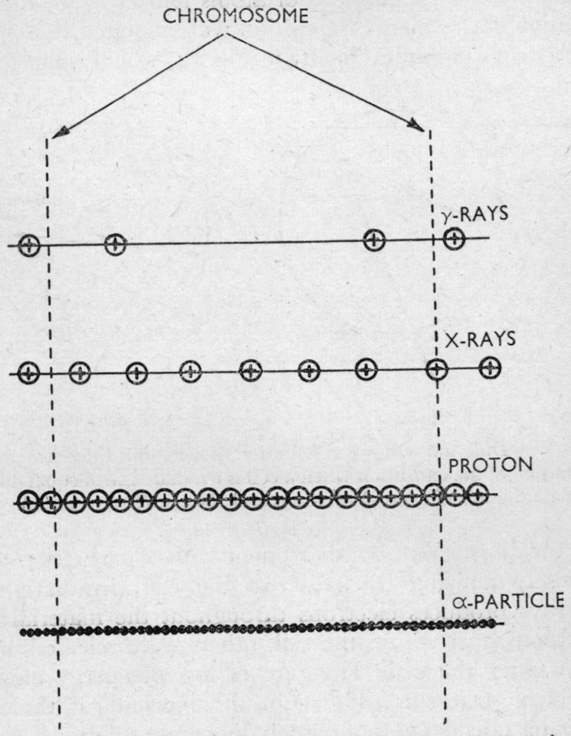

Fig. 15 – Distribution of ionization when a chromosome is exposed to different types of radiation.

protons of energy up to 10 MeV are sufficiently densely ionizing to deposit the right amount of energy but that the average ionization density of the electrons given off by ordinary X- and γ-rays is far below this value. At first sight it would appear as if X- and γ-rays should not break chromosomes at all, but this is not so, since an electron at the end of its track produces a sufficiently high ion density.

On p. 25 it was shown that the rate at which a particle *loses* energy increases as the speed or energy of the particle itself decreases. Consequently at the end of its track when the speed of the electrons has been greatly decreased it loses energy rapidly. To summarize, Lea concluded that a chromosome is broken whenever an α-particle, medium energy proton, or an electron at the very end of its track passes through it. This theory, being in good agreement with all the facts known in Lea's lifetime, was widely accepted.

When it was found that a chromosome abnormality was produced in some cells every time after the passage of only a single α-particle through the nucleus the theory had to be modified, since every particle passing through the nucleus would not be expected to traverse a chromosome. A break was said to be produced every time a particle passed close to as well as through the chromosome. The purely mechanical interpretation had to be strained even more when experiments showed that different pretreatments, such as growth of the cell in medium deficient in certain mineral salts or exposure of the cell to infra-red radiation, increased its sensitivity so that smaller radiation doses produced the same chromosome damage. A further blow to the theory was the discovery that the number of chromosomes broken by a given dose of X- or γ-rays depended on the amount of oxygen in the atmosphere in which the cells were irradiated. In the complete absence of oxygen only about one-third of the breaks are found as if the same irradiation is given in air.* Breaks produced by densely ionizing radiation depend much less on the amount of oxygen present. Almost all the biological changes produced by radiation, ranging from such isolated events as chromosome breaks to the dose necessary for killing an animal, are decreased in the absence of oxygen. This so-called oxygen effect appears to be fundamental to radiobiology and its significance will be discussed

* Increasing the oxygen pressure above that of the air – for example placing the cells in pure oxygen – does not further enhance the efficiency of breakage.

on p. 166. On the purely mechanical interpretation, that the breaks follow the passage of a particle through the chromosome, it is difficult to understand why the concentration of oxygen should be important.

The oxygen effect could be understood much more easily if the action of the radiation involved an inhibition of synthesis, since oxygen can enhance the so-called indirect action of radiation (see p. 181) which may play an important part in the destruction of the system responsible for synthesis. Chemical processes in the cell such as breaking down of the ingested food into smaller molecules and the building up (synthesis) of the materials required by the cell (for example chromosome material) are brought about by the intervention of enzymes. These are highly specific units which can in general perform only one job, and in the synthesis of a complex substance a large number of enzymes are collectively involved. The mechanism by which enzymes can cause specific chemical reaction to take place is not understood; many enzymes have been isolated and found to consist of proteins usually of fairly high molecular weight. Although enzymes are large molecules they are still much smaller than chromosomes or other cell structures. A typical enzyme of molecular weight 100,000 would be a sphere of diameter 0·007 μ while chromosomes have a diameter of the order of 1 μ and cells of 20 μ.* This biochemical view would appear to be further supported by the observation first made by the Hungarian scientist George von Hevesy that the enzyme system responsible for the synthesis of the important constituent of chromosomes, deoxyribonucleic acid (usually abbreviated to DNA) is one of the most sensitive in the cell to radiation. Doses sufficient to produce only a temporary stop in mitosis usually stop DNA synthesis as well without interfering with the working of any of the other cellular enzymes. It would be quite logical for interference with DNA synthesis to produce defects in the chromosomes, which become apparent at metaphase as breaks. However, there is a considerable

* For definition of the length unit μ see p. 25.

amount of evidence which is completely inconsistent with the interpretation. Much of it is too technical to be summarized here, but perhaps most compelling is the fact that the period at which the cell is most sensitive to radiation (i.e. when the number of chromosome breaks produced is greatest for a given dose) does not coincide with the period at which the cell is most active in the manufacture of DNA.

At the present stage of knowledge the most adequate summary is probably that given by P. C. Koller, one of the foremost experts in this field, which has come to be known as cytogenetics:

'The chromosomes are dynamic entities within the cell and it is becoming increasingly evident, indeed, that the chromosomes are not static units with genes lined up like cars in a railroad train. Their structure is not permanent; it is continuously rebuilt from the material of the surrounding medium. The mutagens not only attack the chromosomes already visible but they also interfere with the process of chromosome synthesis. By considering these aspects the phenomenon of chromosome breakage takes up a greater significance; it becomes an essential part of the general biochemical mechanism which underlies cell reaction, adaptation and selection, i.e. evolution.'

DEATH OF THE CELL

Model experiments in test-tubes with enzymes and other materials extracted from the cell prove that doses of radiation of the order of hundreds of thousands of roentgen will produce profound chemical changes. The enzymes are rendered inactive and the rigidity of nucleoprotein gels – the material of which the chromosomes are made up – is decreased; any one of such changes would be sufficient to result in the death of the cell, and the immediate death can probably be attributed to changes in the physical properties of vital cell structure. The very radio-resistant cells, such as those of certain marine algae and amoeba (see Table II, p. 49) are obviously only affected by these gross changes of radiation. Our interest centres on why some cells are killed by a few hundred roentgen and most cells by a few thousand roentgen. With these doses cell death only occurs after a time interval, and immediately after irradiation the cells look and behave apparently quite normally. This delay, which is one of the most characteristic features of radiation injury, can be explained in a number of cases in terms of chromosome breaks. Mitosis is a most delicate and carefully balanced process and any disturbance of the chromosome structure can interfere with it. Since chromosomes are self-perpetuating, any chromosome fault will be reproduced in the next division when once again it has an opportunity of preventing successful mitosis. Frequently radiation damage to chromosomes results in the formation of a micronucleus (see Plate 7a) which can physically obstruct cell division. Chromosome damage cannot of course lead to the death of the cell unless this enters division after irradiation. If a cell is irradiated at the sensitive stage in the resting phase it must reach anaphase before a chromosome defect could possibly bring about its destruction. Chromosomes of a somatic cell (i.e. one that is not actively dividing) can still be broken, but there is no obvious mechanism by which such a break, which can influence only the nucleus and not the cytoplasm, can bring about the death of the cell. Yet there can be no doubt that radiation kills cells which are so highly specialized that they can no longer undergo division, as well as cells which could conceivably divide but which form part of an adult organism and whose growth is controlled so that they only divide when stimulated to repair some physical damage.

In general cells of this type are more radiation-resistant than rapidly dividing cells, and this observation forms the first generalization in radiobiology put forward in 1906 by Bergonié and Tribondeau as follows: 'Cells are sensitive to radiation in proportion to their proliferative activity and in inverse proportion to their degree of differentiation.' This statement has undoubtedly been of the greatest value in the early days of the radiation therapy of cancer, but its limitations are becoming more apparent as the study of radiation effects turns away from purely anatomical observations to dynamic biochemical investigation. There are a number of very pronounced exceptions to Bergonié and Tribondeau's law, the most notable being that lymphocytes – blood cells which are quite incapable of division and have reached the end of their mitotic cycle – are highly radiosensitive and are killed when irradiated in isolation by a few hundred roentgen. Admitting the generalization that somatic cells are more radio-resistant than rapidly dividing ones, they are nevertheless killed in many cases by a few thousand roentgen and much of the destruction of tumour cells in radiation therapy is of this kind. Although tumour cells divide they often do so relatively slowly, and radiation therapy would be totally ineffective if it only affected the small proportion of cells about to divide. Where cells are killed without first entering division there is also a time interval between the irradiation and the visible degeneration indicating death. An elegant experiment first performed with fertilized eggs and subsequently with frogs illustrates perfectly the delay between the irradiation and the appearance of the injury and indicates a possible mechanism other than chromosome breaks. After a lethal dose of radiation frogs will die within three to six weeks if they are kept at ordinary temperature, but if they are stored in a dormant state at a low temperature just above freezing point they will survive for many months. However as soon as the irradiated animals are warmed up they begin to show radiation symptoms and will die in the same time interval as the animals which were not cooled after irradiation. This effect of arresting the course of events following upon radiation by cooling has been found with many radiosensitive animals which survive drastic cooling.

The inference from these experiments is clear; radiation produces a change which itself is not detectable but which is multiplied by the organism in its normal processes until death or a visible injury ensues. By cooling, the normal processes are slowed down or stopped so that the initial damage cannot be increased; however the damage remains and when the frog is warmed it again becomes enhanced. This interpretation derived from biological considerations also provides a perfect explanation for the fact which has worried chemists and physicists, that the dose of radiation sufficient to kill or visibly injure a cell represents such a minute amount of energy that it could only affect a very few molecules, a change totally insufficient to bring about the pronounced biological effects directly.

Up to now attention has been focused on the nucleus, whose essential function is to control cell division; but in a somatic cell the nucleus is probably not so important. Some algae for example can survive for a relatively long time after having their nuclei removed. Important initial injury which the cell's own metabolism turns into a lethal effect may very well be produced in the cytoplasm, which is the power-house of the cell where food is converted into energy needed by the cell to live and to replace its structural compounds. The cell must be considered as a whole since its working depends on an intricate pattern of closely interwoven processes. Because an injury is seen in the nucleus it does not mean that it has originated there. For this reason we cannot disregard what is happening to the cytoplasm.

A great deal of work has been carried out on radiation-induced changes in the biochemical functions of the cell. The Belgian radiobiologist Z. M. Bacq has reviewed this field and reached the unexpected conclusion that radiation of the order of a few thousand roentgen does *not* decrease the activity of any of the enzymes in the cytoplasm and that in a few cases an increase may even be noted if the cell is examined immediately or soon after irradiation. If examination is delayed, decreased activity both in the synthesis of new substances and the breakdown of food is usually observed; these changes, however, do not tell us about the original damage done by the radiation but merely reflect incipient cell death when the ordinary processes of metabolism are naturally running down. Similar changes would be found whatever the cause of death.

The paradoxical conclusion that a lethal agent may initially cause some metabolic processes to proceed faster than normal may provide a valuable clue to the nature of the initial injury. If a growth-stimulating substance whose controlled release is vital to the life of the cell were suddenly set free by radiation an immediate burst of metabolic activity would be followed by a gradual slowing down of the workings of the cell owing to the wasteful depletion of this factor. Bacq and his collaborators at Liège University have some evidence for the existence of such a vital substance whose isolation would be an event of the first magnitude and the importance of which would extend far beyond the field of radiation biology.

A more general kind of interference with the processes in either the cytoplasm or the nucleus may also fit the facts, and is discussed in more detail in Chapter 10. There are two ways by which the efficient running of a factory can be interfered with; some of the machines can be put out of action, or the internal organization, whereby material flows smoothly from one machine to the next to give the finished products, can be disrupted. As we have seen, isolated processes (or machines) – i.e. the activity of individual enzyme systems – are not arrested by irradiation, but perhaps it may be that the internal structure of the cytoplasm is disturbed. The cytoplasm appears to those who observe it through a microscope as a chaotic part of the cell showing nothing of the order and precision of the nucleus at mitosis. The various cytoplasmic particles rush about in a random manner and there appears to be no organization among them. The biochemist who studies the wonderful chemical processes which are conducted in the cytoplasm realizes that there must be an impressive order for this factory to function. In these minute spaces not one but hundreds of chemical reactions are carried out simultaneously. The complexity of many of these processes is very much greater than that of any reaction which can be carried out in a laboratory. To consider one example only, the synthesis of proteins from amino-acids, a reaction which has so far completely defied the ingenuity of chemists, takes place with the greatest efficiency in the cell. These reactions are controlled by a large number of different enzymes, the majority of which are situated in the small granules of the cytoplasm. Now it is clear that the different enzymes have to be strictly localized, so that the chain of processes will go smoothly. In the same cell there are enzymes which break down proteins and others which build them up from smaller units; if they got mixed up chaos would result and the life of the cell could not be long sustained. Cutting through a potato with a knife brings about such a disorganization which soon becomes visible. In the cytoplasm of potato cells there is a complex substance – dihydroxyphenylalanine – which is oxidized by the enzyme tyrosinase, also present in the potato, into a brown resin known as melanin and similar to the brown pigment in skin. In the undamaged cell the two are kept apart and no brown substance is formed. On cutting the potato the two can get together and a brown stain appears along the cut. If radiation disrupted some of the internal structures responsible for maintaining this order no *initial* decrease in any enzymatic activity would be noted; indeed the release of the enzymes from their specific location might temporarily increase their activity. The cell would, however, be severely damaged as the result of the disorder. This mechanism, to which reference will again be made in Chapter 10, is consistent with many of the facts, but direct proof that such changes are produced by radiation is lacking.

In summary, one can probably say that radiation produces at least two types of injury in the cell; the first is seen as chromosome breaks, and these can bring about the death of the cell. The other injury, the nature of which is as yet unknown, holds up the normal cell cycle for a time. The killing of cells which are not actively dividing is probably closely related to the arrest of cell division observed in dividing cells. The relative contribution of these two mechanisms to the overall effect of radiations is probably not the same for different tissues and cells, and much needless confusion has been produced by researchers who claim that one or other of these effects is all-important. It is necessary to guard against over-emphasizing the importance of visible chromosome changes just because they are readily seen and fascinating to study. The current trend of research is towards determining the more obscure and elusive injuries which cannot be seen under the microscope.

CHAPTER 3

RADIATION SICKNESS

MAMMALS are exceptionally sensitive to radiation. Table III on p. 74 shows that there are considerable variations in the radiosensitivity of different mammals. None of these figures are absolute as they depend on the strain of the given animal: there are mice which have been selectively bred for high or low radiation resistance, and by successive brother-sister matings so-called pure strains are obtained which show more uniform behaviour and have a smaller

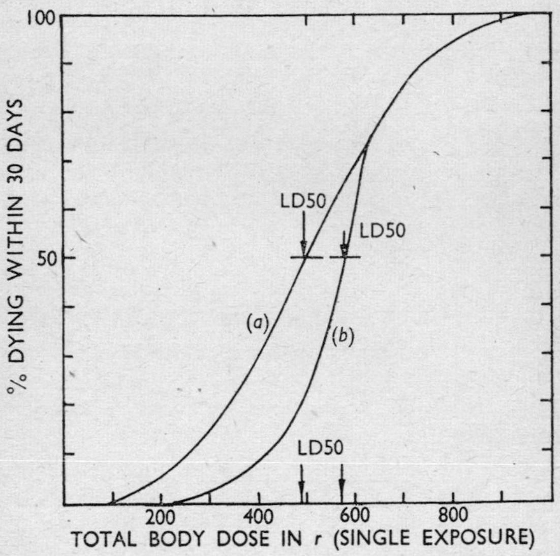

Fig. 16 – Graph relating the number of mice killed by different doses of X-rays. Curve (*a*) gives results with a 'wild' strain in which there is a much wider variation between different animals than with a closely inbred strain, which is represented by curve (*b*).

variation (see Fig. 16). The lethal dose may vary by as much as 30 per cent between these strains. Other factors also have a minor influence on the radiation sensitivity; it has been found that in some cases females are able to sustain a 10 per cent greater dose than males. Body weight appears to have very little influence; this is surprising, since the total amount of energy deposited by a given dose of radiation is proportional to the weight of the animal. More energy, therefore, will be left in a fat than in a lean animal. Increase in age substantially lowers resistance to radiation; the lethal dose for 18-month-old rats was 30 per cent less than that of young adults (three months) from the same strain. This is a most important finding since it complements the observation which is discussed in detail on p. 92 that small doses of radiation produce premature ageing.

As already mentioned, animals in hibernation are remarkably resistant, and doses of many thousands of roentgen are necessary to kill marmots or squirrels while they are dormant. On warming, the animals will behave as if they had been irradiated in the non-hibernating state. The bat appeared to be the one remarkable exception amongst mammals in that the lethal dose observed was of the order of 15,000 r, i.e. it was twenty to fifty times more resistant than other mammals. Admittedly it is a hibernating species, but the experiments were carried out at ordinary temperatures when the animals should be normal. But these bats did not eat in captivity and this lowered their metabolic rate to a state equivalent to hibernation and was responsible for the apparent radiation resistance. Bats which were eating succumbed to 700 r.

It is now possible to cool small mammals such as mice to a temperature only two or three degrees above freezing point and to return them without harm to ordinary temperature a few hours later. If they are irradiated at these low temperatures they are truly radiation-resistant (that is, even after they have been warmed up) and can tolerate two to three times the dose which normally would kill them. The reason for this resistance is that their tissues are deficient in oxygen while cold, and this protects against radiation (see p. 166).

For obvious reasons no accurate data for man are available, and a value can only be deduced from the casualties of the atomic bomb explosions at Hiroshima and Nagasaki. A fairly good estimate of the radiation intensity at different distances from the explosion centres can be made, and the approximate dose received by individuals in different regions can be calculated. The majority of injuries were due to blast and the frightful burns produced by the intense heat given off at the flash of the explosion. From victims who escaped death from these effects information was obtained about the effects of γ-radiation. Within 1,000 metres (five-eighths of a mile) the dose received was more than 1,000 r, and none who were caught in the open survived for more than one week. In the zone between 1,000 and 1,250 metres (dose received about 700 r) those fatally injured died within two months, but there were a few who appeared to have recovered. From Table III it can be seen that in the order

TABLE III

The resistance of different mammals to X-rays expressed as the dose necessary to kill half the animals within 30 days (LD50 30 days). These values are not absolute but vary from one strain to another

Guinea-pig	200–400 r	Mouse	400–600 r
Swine	275 r	Rat	600–700 r
Dog	325 r	Hamster	700 r
Goat	350 r	Rabbit	800 r
Monkey	500 r		

of radiation resistance man ranks between the goat and the mouse, and is roughly as sensitive as a monkey. In this table the radiation dose is expressed as the lethal dose required to kill 50 per cent of the animals in 30 days (abbreviated to LD50/30 days). The reason why we do not choose the dose required to kill 100 per cent is that in any group there is a natural variation in resistance; some animals succumb more easily than others and occasionally there are animals which are very much more hardy. This type of behaviour is shown in Fig. 16. If in an experiment one attempts to find the dose which kills all animals the value recorded will depend on the chance of having included any of those that are resistant. In a series of experiments the values recorded for the 100 per cent lethal dose will vary considerably. The dose required to kill approximately half the animals can be determined much more precisely, and this value is then remarkably constant from experiment to experiment. The reason for having a definite time limit within which death occurs will become apparent from the discussion on p. 77.

All the figures given apply when the whole of the animal has been irradiated. Even if only small parts of the body are not irradiated, such as the tail of a rat, the lethal dose is substantially increased. This is brought out clearly in Table IV, where mice were given 1,025 r, a dose substantially greater than that necessary to kill them all; 100 per cent lethality would probably have been obtained with 700–800 r. Yet after shielding different parts of the animals there were varying numbers of survivors, showing that the LD50 had been substantially increased by not exposing a small part of the animal: protecting the spleen is outstandingly effective and will be discussed again in another connexion on p. 175. In the experiments shown in Table IV the different tissues were shielded by enclosing them in a sheet of lead through which the X-rays cannot penetrate.

TABLE IV

Survival of mice after 1,025 r of X-rays (a dose which is greatly in excess of that necessary to kill all unshielded animals) after protection of different tissues

Tissue protected	*Percentage surviving thirty days*	*Tissue protected*	*Percentage surviving thirty days*
None	0	Head	28
Kidney	0	Liver	33
Hind leg	13	Spleen	78
Intestine	27		

The animal can survive tremendous doses to isolated parts. It is usual practice to irradiate tumours with many thousands of roentgen of X-rays without hazarding the general health of the patient. Yet one-tenth of this dose given to the whole body would be fatal. Even with localized irradiation exposure of certain parts is more harmful to the animal than that of others. Rajewsky working in Germany used a most ingenious method to detect the critical organs. He shielded the whole body of the rat with lead except for a narrow slit, the position of which was progressively changed. The most sensitive organs were those situated in the abdomen (the liver, spleen, kidney, and part of the intestine) but it was not possible to pinpoint any one of these. To kill the animal it was necessary to give doses of the order of 8,000 r through this narrow slit even when it exposed part of the critical area. Shielding of parts of the body from the radiation not only reduces the lethal effects but with sub-lethal doses cuts down pathological change such as induction of leukaemia (see Chapter 5).

THE LETHAL DOSE

The statement can probably be accepted that all exposure to ionizing radiation is harmful. In view of the general background of radiation (see p. 122) one must not exaggerate the importance of small doses. It is probably true that prolonged exposure to sunlight can lead to skin cancer, and is the reason for the higher incidence of such tumours among people who work out of doors, but the remedy is clearly not a mole-like existence without daylight, any more than the denial of the enormous benefits of atomic energy is the answer to the problematical dangers of a small increase in the radiation background.

We have to distinguish between a dose of radiation given within a relatively short period and chronic irradiation. Since the body shows a remarkable capacity for recovery from radiation it can withstand repeated small doses which if given over a shorter period or even in one irradiation would be fatal. Since these recovery processes take many hours there is no difference between a dose of, for example, 600 r given within one minute at the rate of 600 r/min. or in one hour at 10 r/min. However if the rate is cut down to 1 r/min., the radiation symptoms are very much less, and the dose required to kill within thirty days will be more than doubled. If the dose rate is reduced still further, say to 1 r/hour, then the animal can tolerate this for very long periods, and a reduction in the total life-span can be observed only after receiving *in toto* a dose approximately five to six times that necessary to produce death within thirty days if given at a higher dose rate (see Fig. 17).

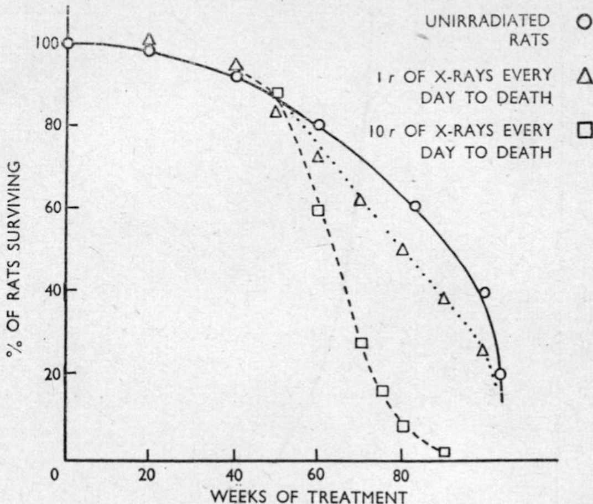

Fig. 17 – Continuous irradiation with 10 r per day shows a shortening of the life span. The effect from 1 r per day is rather doubtful. All the animals would die within 30 days following a single dose of 800 r if given within an hour or so. Yet after 11½ weeks the animals receiving 10 r per day have received 800 r but none have died. (Data from H. A. Blair.)

However, there are long-term effects due to genetic changes which are independent of dose rate. That is to say they occur to the same extent whether the dose is given rapidly or slowly. In practice they are more apparent when the dose is given slowly, since the symptoms of radiation sickness are then absent or much less severe. These long-term effects which are transmitted to the progeny of irradiated animals will be described in the next two chapters.

Radiation sickness, which forms the subject of this chapter, can be considered in the same way as poisoning; the consequences may be fatal, or they may give rise to illness with certain symptoms which disappear in time. Where a single dose of X-rays of less than 200 r is given there is no detectable shortening of the life-span in mice or rats (the animals on which most of the experiments have

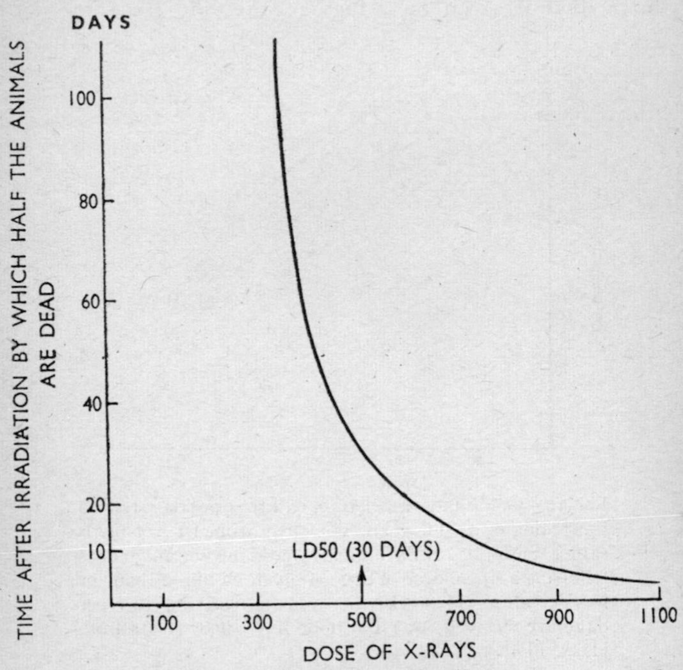

Figs. 18 and 19 – Effect of different doses of radiation given at a single exposure on the survival time of mice. The value chosen is the time by which half the animals have died. From the curves the LD50 dose for different times of death is obtained. The LD50 in thirty days is about 500 r for these mice.

been carried out), although symptoms of radiation sickness appear some time after irradiation (see p. 84). However, the incidence of tumours many months after the irradiation is greater than in unirradiated animals, and cancer becomes prominent as a cause of death. In view of the long latent period between irradiation and the appearance of malignant growths (see Chapter 5) their effect on the life expectancy of experimental animals is difficult to determine. Though almost all of the pioneer doctors using X-rays died of cancer, most of them lived for twenty to thirty years after severe over-exposure to radiations. Their lives were shortened, but not by very much.

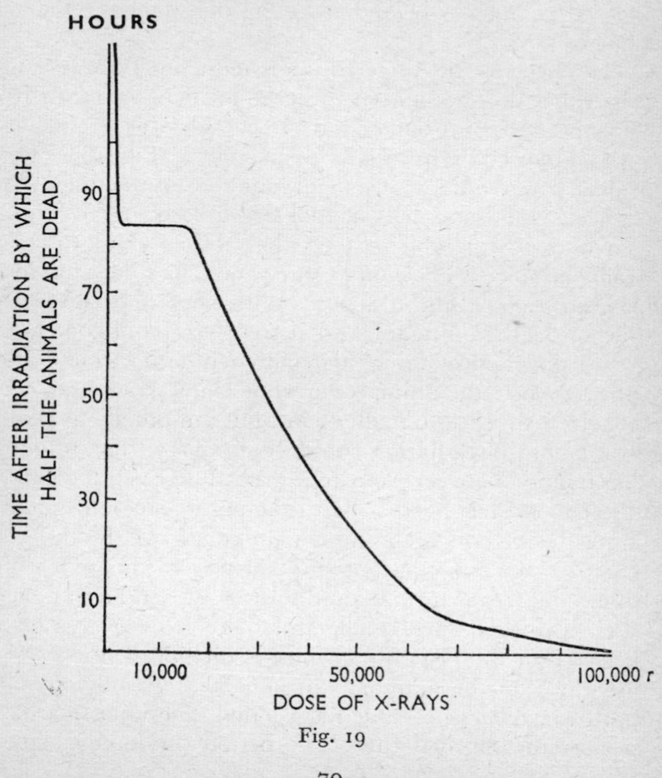

Fig. 19

With more than 200 r of X-rays death occurs prematurely, i.e. the lethal action of the radiation is recognizable. As the dose is increased beyond this point the time for 50 per cent of the animals to die falls sharply. The complete dose mortality curve for a strain of white mice irradiated with X-rays is shown in Figs. 18 and 19. From the first graph it can be seen that the LD50 with 350 r is 100 days. This is probably less than half the life expectancy of unirradiated mice, the exact value for which varies somewhat from laboratory to laboratory. After this the mortality rate increases rapidly and 500 r gives LD50 in thirty days. Increasing the dose beyond this reduces the time for death relatively more slowly, and at 1,000 r this reaches three and a half days.

The effect of still larger doses is most remarkable, since these doses do not shorten the time for death any further. To bring this point out we have to consider the results with a graph plotted on quite a different scale. In Fig. 18 we were dealing with deaths in days and hundreds of roentgen, now we need hours and tens of thousands of roentgen. This is seen in Fig. 19, which shows that the survival time for irradiated mice is constant at three and a half days for doses between 1,000 r and 15,000 r. With very high doses the time for death falls again, and at 100,000 r is only one hour. We are now approaching the region of instantaneous death; with 200,000 r the animals die while being irradiated, even though with exceptionally powerful equipment available this amount of radiation could be given in a few minutes. This relation between dose and survival time is not confined to mice, and has been shown to apply to rats and guinea-pigs as well, though the numerical values for the different stages differ. The constant survival period for guinea-pigs is four and a quarter days and for rats two and a half days. These variations are small, and there is every reason to believe that the response of mice is qualitatively representative of that for mammals in general. It is obvious now that there is no one value for a lethal dose unless one also specifies the survival time. The period commonly chosen, thirty days, is very informative, since the survival time rises sharply when doses fall below this value, and after a reduction by as little as one third a decrease in survival time already becomes difficult to establish experimentally.

Different radiations. So far only the effects of X- and γ-rays have been discussed; that is radiations giving rise to low ion density tracks or having a low rate of loss of energy (see p. 23). More densely ionizing radiations are more effective in producing effects on isolated cells than radiations of low ion density (see p. 206), and it is not surprising that this also applies to the death of mammals. Since it is necessary to irradiate the whole body of the animal it is not possible to compare the effects of particulate radiations such as α-particles or protons from an external source since these radiations would hardly penetrate the skin because their range in tissues is only a small fraction of an inch. Extremely large doses of such radiation are therefore necessary to produce radiation sickness and death within thirty days, since only part of the body is being irradiated. These radiations produce intense local skin reactions, but do not kill. The same applies when animals are irradiated with β-rays, which do not differ in ionization density from X-rays or γ-rays but which cannot penetrate deeply; with these a dose ten times that for X-rays is necessary to kill mammals. These findings emphasize again the great increase in resistance to radiation which results if part of the body is unirradiated and is able to begin repair processes.

Neutrons have a very great range, for reasons discussed on p. 34, and can be used in the same way as hard X- and γ-rays to produce uniform irradiation of the whole body. They give rise to protons inside the irradiated tissue, and these have a much higher ionizing density than the electrons released by the X- and γ-rays used in work of this type. No single figure can be quoted for the ratio of the effectiveness of fast neutrons to that of therapy X-rays (e.g. 200 kV) since different values are obtained depending on the exact conditions of irradiation. For lethal effects at reasonable dose rates neutrons are about three times as effective as X-rays. In other words it is necessary to deposit only one-third of the amount of energy when this is derived from neutrons as compared with that needed when this is derived from X-rays.

Something approximating to a whole body irradiation with α-rays can be achieved by causing the animal to inhale the gas radon which emits α-particles and distributes itself fairly uniformly through the body. In this way it was found that this radiation was about twice as effective as neutrons (i.e. five to six times as effective as X-rays) in producing acute death, illustrating the danger of densely ionizing radiations. The body is able to recover less from the radiation of higher specific ionization than it does after exposure to X-rays and γ-rays, and the relative effectiveness of neutrons becomes even greater when chronic effects at low dose rates are studied. This can be seen by comparing the recovery in an organ with frequently dividing cells, such as the spleen, after irradiation with X-rays and with neutrons, with a dose which produces in each case a high proportion of cell death. The appearance of the organ a day or so after irradiation will be the same, but after about a week regeneration and new cell colonies will be seen only in the animal irradiated with X-rays. Consequently the destructive action of neutrons does not fall off nearly so rapidly as that of X-rays on decreasing the dose rate. Thus chronic effects can be produced by repeated exposure to fast neutrons at one-tenth or even less of the dose necessary with X- or γ-irradiation. This applies particularly to the incidence of opacities in the lens of the eye, eventually leading to cataract, so safety precautions when working with fast neutrons must be much more stringent than those for X- or γ-rays. Besides being more effective the effects of densely ionizing radiations are sometimes qualitatively different. The symptoms after irradiation with neutrons are not the same as those observed after exposure to X- and γ-rays, and the cause of death would appear to be different.

Although exposure to α- and β-ray-emitting isotopes is much less hazardous than exposure to isotopes emitting γ-rays, because of the lack of penetration, the former become dangerous if they are inhaled, since they may become widely distributed and thereby give rise to a whole body dose or become fixed in certain organs, when they often induce cancer (see p. 149). For this reason strict safety precautions must be observed in handling radioactive materials, even if the radiation dose received from them by external irradiation is very small. The β-ray emitting radioactive dust which contaminates enormous areas after nuclear explosion is likely to produce more casualties than the momentary flash of neutrons and γ-rays released during the explosion.

THE CAUSE OF DEATH

The symptoms of acute radiation sickness are summarized in Table v, but these tell us little about the cause of death. If a pathologist carries out a post-mortem examination on a mammal which has succumbed after a radiation dose of a few hundred roentgen he would find it very difficult to pinpoint death to failure of a particular organ. He would find internal haemorrhages of varying severities, and in some cases, though by no means all, they would be considered to be the cause of death; haemorrhage can kill either by destroying the function of a vital organ or by producing severe anaemia. But the site at which haemorrhage is found varies in different animals; in rats and mice it is confined almost entirely to the intestine, where it would not be lethal; whereas, in the pig, haemorrhages are also found near the heart where they could kill. Now anaemia is observed in all animals after irradiation, though death often occurs before this is really severe. If anaemia causes death, then blood transfusions ought to prevent it, but in practice no increase in survival or even significant increase in the time between irradiation and death is found by giving extensive transfusions.

TABLE V

Symptoms of radiation sickness from observations made in Japan

TIME AFTER EXPOSURE	600 r (*lethal dose*)	400 r (*median lethal dose*)	200 r (*moderate dose*)
FIRST WEEK	Nausea and vomiting after 2 hours	Nausea and vomiting after 2 hours	
	No definite symptoms	No definite symptoms	No definite symptoms
	Diarrhoea, vomiting inflammation of throat		
SECOND WEEK	Fever, rapid emaciation leading to death (100 per cent)		
THIRD WEEK		Loss of hair begins Loss of appetite General malaise Fever and pallor leading to rapid emaciation and death for 50 per cent of the population	
			Loss of hair Loss of appetite Sore throat Pallor and diarrhoea Recovery begins (no deaths in absence of complications)

After irradiation the body loses some of its ability to produce antibodies which combat invasion by bacteria against which it is normally immune (see p. 100) and following an atomic explosion the surgeon finds that even minor wounds become septic, in spite of the most rigorous precautions. As a result, infection is almost invariably seen after a whole body dose of a few hundred roentgen. Because of the haemorrhages in the intestines the body is invaded by bacteria from this source, and such infections of course are extremely dangerous, but if they were the ultimate cause of death, treatment with antibiotics should decrease mortality. The effect of these modern drugs is dramatic whereever a disease is brought about by bacterial infection, especially since a number of different types, capable between them of destroying most kinds of bacteria, are now available. Yet the effect of these drugs in radiation sickness is far from spectacular; there is some evidence that a combination of antibiotics can produce a slight increase in the time between the lethal dose and death, but the mortality rate is not decreased; in other words treatment with antibiotics does not increase the resistance of the animals to a lethal dose. This proves that infection alone is not the cause of death, but it does not mean that for people who have been irradiated these infections need not be treated. With marginal doses effective treatment of the infection with antibiotics may make all the difference and it can also change the course of the sickness; for example, after irradiation rats suffer from severe diarrhoea, which contributes to death because the loss of water and salts disturbs the normal metabolism; if treated with the antibiotic, aureomycin, the diarrhoea disappears, but the animal dies none the less, although a few days later than it would have done so without treatment. When newly hatched chicks are irradiated their kidneys fail to act, and in this case it is possible to attribute death to damage in one specific organ, but this is very unusual. In view of these variations it may appear that radiation sickness is an ill-defined condition and that it should not be considered as a whole. Indeed, some have held the view that since the symptoms and apparent causes of death are different for different animals, the fundamental mechanism leading to death is different, too.

No complete explanation can be given for the paradox that although the pathological changes from whole body irradiation are diffuse and ill-defined, yet death occurs with remarkable regularity. The problem must be different from poisoning with chemical substances, which have to penetrate through the body and eventually become localized in certain organs. Initially radiation acts equally on all cells, since it does not have to rely for its dissemination on transport by the circulating fluids, such as the blood stream. As a result damage is very widespread; for example, every part of the bone-marrow is affected and no parts are available to undertake repair; this is clearly shown by the increase in survival which occurs when very small parts of the body are shielded against the radiation (see p. 75). The whole of radiation sickness is a complex interplay between cellular damage and impaired recovery processes; this introduces the great diversity and apparent lack of specificity. After whole body irradiation mitosis is stopped, blood production ceases in the bone-marrow, and the walls of the intestine are no longer replaced by new cells as they get worn away. Microscopic examination of these organs will show them to be completely devoid of new cells a day after a whole body irradiation of several hundred roentgen. Yet this same effect is produced with doses which do not kill, and no difference can be seen one or two days after irradiation between animals which have received a lethal dose and those which have been given a slightly smaller dose which does not kill. The inhibition of cell division is only temporary, and the bone-marrow and the walls of the intestine begin to fill up with cells again, three or four days after irradiation, so that at the time of death these organs do not appear to have been severely damaged; yet there can be no doubt that the act of putting them temporarily out of commission contributed to death. Presumably by the time these radiosensitive organs are producing cells again the opportunity for repair and recovery of other irradiated cells has been lost.

The great interdependence of the different organs and

cells in the body may be the reason why mammals are so much more susceptible to radiations than most unicellular organisms. The effect of irradiating one organ is often to impair the function of another, which need not even have been exposed to radiation. By irradiating the whole body the balance between organs is disturbed, and a vicious circle is set up: a disturbed condition persists for several days, brought about largely by the fall in blood cells, which in turn are not being replaced by the bone-marrow. By the time the individual cells have recovered, it is too late for the delicate interplay between the different organs to be re-established, and the complex machine comes to a standstill. One might almost say that it is the diversity and the absence of any specific response which is the cause of death. Ionizing radiations hit mammals at their weakest point: the co-ordination of function at the level where it is beyond the control of the brain. The brain and central nervous system are remarkably radiation-resistant, and there is no indication that impairment of these plays any part in radiation sickness.

EFFECTS FOLLOWING NON-LETHAL DOSES*

When considering the injuries following doses of radiation which are not lethal, it is necessary to differentiate between long- and short-term effects. The long-term effects are those which become noticeable only a considerable time after the radiation is given, and when all the immediate signs of radiation have disappeared and are probably forgotten.

* The discussion is confined to X- and γ-rays. Irradiation with densely ionizing radiations produces the same symptoms but at very much lower doses. The relative importance of the different injuries and the time at which they appear are different for different radiations. The densely ionizing rays such as neutrons are more effective than X- and γ-rays, but the magnitude of this difference – the relative biological effectiveness (RBE) see p. 206 – is not the same for different effects produced. As already mentioned (see p. 81) the RBE of densely ionizing particles is greater when the comparison is made at low as opposed to high dose rates.

These delayed effects may also arise after periods of continued exposure to radiation at a low intensity, so that no immediate symptoms become apparent. Besides the time factor there is another characteristic difference; the damage giving rise to immediate effects – radiation sickness – is quickly repaired by the body and the severity of the symptoms is therefore very dependent on the rate at which the radiation is received. The injuries which become apparent as late changes seem to be irreparable, or at best only incompletely reparable, and are therefore much less dependent on dose rate. This is the reason why radiation at very low intensity may fail to produce any symptoms typical of radiation sickness, while still bringing about long-term injuries, some of which will be dealt with in the next two chapters.

Radiation sickness can be of two types: the one follows a single large dose and the other small doses repeated over long periods. The so-called critical dose in a single irradiation is about 100 r, and below this no unpleasant symptoms, such as vomiting and general lethargy, are observed. Blood tests (see below) can reveal a single exposure between 25 and 50 r, but below this dose no pathological changes can be found. Symptoms of radiation sickness also occur after repeated radiation with low intensities, although the appearance of long-delayed effects complicates the picture. From a study in Britain, Sweden, and the U.S.A. of hospital personnel connected with radiation therapy, it would appear that a dose of less than 1 r per week produces definite, though slight, symptoms after several years. However, the effect is small and in animals any harmful effects can only be recognized following continual irradiations with more than 5 r per week. If this dose is given throughout life a shortening in life-span in mice can just be detected, although much higher doses are necessary for this to become marked (see Fig. 17). The safety or tolerance doses are not dictated by considerations of radiation sickness, but rather by the dangers from long-term effects (see Chap. 4). This is the reason why the internationally accepted level of X- and

γ-radiation to which research and industrial workers and hospital staff can be exposed without harm is set as low as 0·3 r in any one week, and it has been suggested that the tolerance dose should be reduced to 0·1 r/week. If a particularly hazardous operation results in the worker getting, for example, 0·02 r/hour, then he can only do this work for fifteen hours in the week and for the rest of the time must stay away from all radiations. In Britain only a very small proportion of those engaged on work involving substances or machines which give off atomic radiations receive the full tolerance dose, and the majority of the staff at Harwell, for example, receive less than one tenth of this dose.

For densely ionizing radiations, such as neutrons or X-rays, no definite safe level has been proposed, since the data on which a recommendation could be based have not yet been obtained. We do know that they are much more effective in producing many types of injury than the sparsely ionizing radiations, and at present one prefers to err on the side of safety and set a tolerance equivalent to 0·01 r per week for these radiations.

Course of illness. When a single heavy dose is received, as it was at Hiroshima and Nagasaki, the victims can be divided into three groups,* and the course of the sickness for these

* The same sequence of events was also found with the Japanese fishermen who accidentally received lethal doses from the radioactive fall-out following the test explosion of the first hydrogen bomb, the force of which greatly exceeded expectations. Very much has been learned about the details of severe radiation sickness from the clinical history of eight physicists who received large doses of radiation in an accident which occurred at the American atomic research laboratories at Los Alomos. In an experiment to demonstrate that an explosive chain reaction sets in when two pieces of polonium exceeding a critical size are brought together, the hands of Dr Louis Slotin slipped, and he and his colleague received whole body doses exceeding 600 r which ended in death on the ninth and twenty-fourth day. Bystanders who received a smaller dose recovered. In spite of the most intense efforts made to save them nothing could be done to stave off the total collapse of the two scientists who died. The progress of the disease could not be influenced by any treatment.

categories is summarized in Table v, which applies when there are no complicating factors due to burns or other injuries. The most remarkable feature of the whole illness is that, apart from attacks of severe vomiting which set in within an hour or so after irradiation, the victim has no indication that he has received a fatal or near-fatal dose. If a dose in excess of 600 r has been received death is almost certain, and a few days after the dose the patient is obviously very ill. His temperature rises and he loses weight very rapidly because he can take no nourishment. The linings of the stomach have been so severely damaged that food can no longer be absorbed. Within two weeks or a month at most death occurs, and so far there is no treatment which can be given to human beings which alters the progress of these events. The methods of assisting recovery, described in Chapter 7, are not sufficiently advanced to be used clinically.

If the vomiting stops after a day or two the dose received is in the lethal range; that is, a considerable proportion, but not all, of those affected will die (dose about 300 to 500 r), but the outcome is not necessarily fatal. For one or two weeks there are no well-defined or distressing symptoms, and even the general feeling of lassitude which sets in a day or so after the irradiation may wear off. But quite suddenly a variety of signs due to infection and anaemia are observed, as well as loss of hair and diarrhoea. From then on the patient may go steadily downhill or may recover, although he will not feel completely fit for some months. Prompt treatment of infections probably increases the chance of survival, but on the whole the outcome is almost entirely dependent on the make-up of the individual, and apart from rather obvious medical measures there is little scope for the physician to influence the course of the illness.

Doses of the order of 200 r produce no immediate symptoms, and if uncomplicated by other factors should not prove fatal. After two or three weeks a general feeling of ill-heath becomes apparent, followed by other symptoms of a more definite type. Anaemia will take longest to disappear, and it may be several months before complete recovery has been achieved; 100 r or less does not bring about any obvious symptoms of illness and only a blood count shows that the irradiation has occurred. A single dose of the order of 25 r produces no observable effects, and can probably be accepted as a calculated risk under certain conditions.

Fortunately no data are available for man of continued irradiation at relatively high dose levels, and human experience of protracted exposure is limited to doses which give rise at the most to changes in the blood picture, but none that cause death by radiation. Experience with experimental animals indicates that with continuous irradiation with more than 50 r per day the symptoms are the same as for a single large dose, except that they will set in after many weeks when the total dose received is several times the lethal dose for a single irradiation. Smaller daily doses right down to 2 or 3 r per day can still be considered lethal, since they definitely shorten life, but the illness now has a quite different character. None of the typical symptoms such as diarrhoea, severe anaemia, or loss of appetite and weight, are observed, and the changes seen can best be summarized as being akin to those normally associated with old age. Continuous irradiation with doses which do not exceed 25 r per day may be said to age the animals prematurely. The data in Fig. 17 can be taken to show that the lethal dose (LD50) of X-rays given at the rate of 10 r per day is 6,500 r. A more useful way of looking at the results is that continued irradiation of 10 r/day lowers the life-span (expressed as the period in which half the animals have died) of the rat from ninety-five weeks to sixty-five weeks. In the same series of experiments 1 r per day lowered the time necessary for half the animals to die to seventy-eight weeks. Even as little as 0·1 r per day may have produced some reduction in life-span.

A large single dose which does not kill also leaves a permanent mark which is revealed as premature ageing. There is an increase in the incidence of cancer a long time after irradiation (see Chapter 5) and this will contribute to a decrease in life expectancy. But even when allowance has been made for such deaths, irradiated animals still die sooner than normal ones (see Fig. 20). No specific cause for these earlier deaths can be given and they follow the same pattern as those of ordinary animals dying

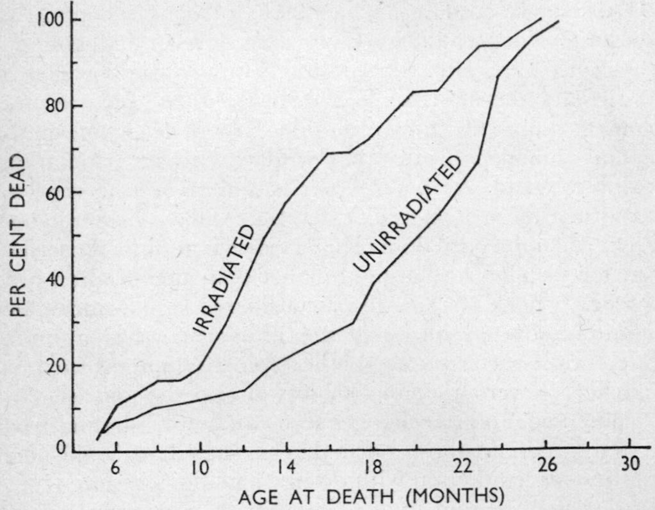

Fig. 20 – Influence on life expectancy of mice of a single dose of 500 r of X-rays, which failed to kill an appreciable number of this strain. Since it is known that irradiation can produce cancer (see Chapter 5) all animals which died from cancer or leukaemia were excluded from this comparison.

of old age. Some investigators believe that atomic radiations hasten the onset of typical senile alteration and can be considered to accelerate ageing.

Effect on the blood. There are two circulating fluids in mammals which are responsible for supplying every part of the body with food derived from the digestive organs and with oxygen from the lungs. In addition they have to dispose of waste products, which are eventually eliminated by the excretory organs, and of carbon dioxide which is exhaled.

The blood circulates through a closed system of tubes and is pumped very efficiently by the heart. The whole round trip through the body and lung and back to its starting-point only takes about two minutes. All tissue is bathed in fluid which exudes from the finest capillaries carrying the blood and is collected again and returned to the veins by lymph vessels which ensure the forward flow of the liquid. To fulfil its purpose the blood contains cells which originate in the blood-producing organs from which they are discharged into the blood stream where they perform different specific functions. After a certain time the blood cells deteriorate and are then disposed of by the spleen or alimentary canal. Under normal circumstances the blood cells are replaced as required by the blood-forming organs which carry, however, a reserve supply for release in emergency such as a haemorrhage. The volume of tissue fluid is kept in balance by the intake of drink and its distribution between the blood and tissue is complex, involving a number of factors and organs.

The red cells are by far the most common, and there are about 500 of these to every one of the others, which are known as white cells and consist of many different types. The main division is into lymphocytes, which are made in the lymph glands, and granulocytes, which are produced in the bone-marrow; the latter can be divided into a number of sub-groups, the most common of which are the neutrophils. Since lymph tissue is spread throughout the body, nothing short of total body irradiation will influence all the sites at which they are produced, but for the same reason it is almost impossible to irradiate any part of the body without exposing some lymphoid tissue. Lymphocyte counts are therefore a very sensitive biological indicator for detecting irradiation. The red cells and the various types of granulocytes are formed in the bone-marrow and a few other organs, from one and the same basic cell, the reticulocytes. This is the precursor of a number of cell types and environmental conditions determine the kind of differentiation they undergo to become a particular type of mature blood cell.

Once they have acquired their full degree of specialization they are no longer capable of division, and new cells needed for replacement are produced by division of the reticulocytes.

The lifetime of the cells varies greatly; lymphocytes survive for less than a day; granulocytes live for about three days; while the same red cells carry on for three or four months before they break up and have to be replaced. A short-lived blood component of the greatest importance is the platelets, which are related to the granulocytes and carry enzymes that are necessary if blood clotting is to occur. Platelets are therefore vital for the control of haemorrhages and if there are too few present, small injuries – particularly internal ones – which would normally be quite harmless, may prove fatal.

Radiation to the whole body affects all the different cells of the blood, but as with all radiation injuries these changes

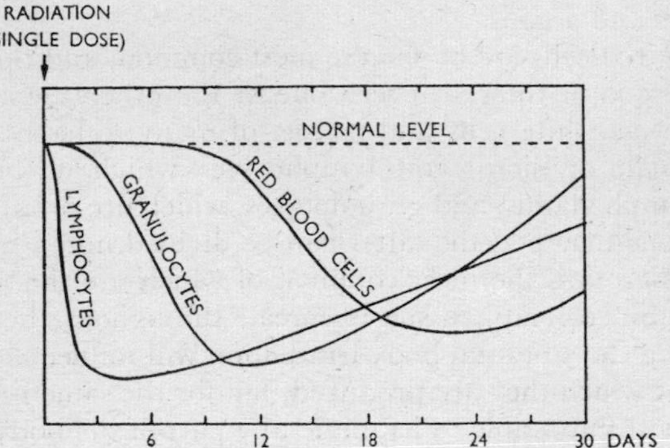

Fig. 21 – Effect of a single dose of X-rays of about 300 r on the different cells in the blood.

only become noticeable some time after irradiation. The general pattern for a dose which does not kill is shown in Fig. 21. A reduction in the number of lymphocytes can be recognized less than one hour after irradiation. In addition to giving a very early indication, a significant drop in lymphocytes is found in man and animals after as little as one dose of 25 r of total body irradiation. This great sensitivity is due to the fact that the circulating lymphocytes have such a very short life, and any interference with cell division in the lymph-forming tissue is bound to be reflected very quickly in the blood picture. In addition the lymphocytes themselves are very radio-sensitive and radiation may shorten their life and thereby aggravate the shortage resulting from the hold-up in mitosis. With less than lethal doses a gradual upward trend in the lymphocyte count can be observed after three days, but the subsequent rate of recovery is rather slow. For doses in the lethal range where some of the animals survive, the lymphocyte count does not begin to recover for about two weeks and in the early stages gives no indication whether an animal will survive or not. The low number of lymphocytes is not thought to be critical to the animal and does not contribute to the more serious aspect of radiation sickness, but it is diagnostically most useful.

The fall in granulocytes can be observed only a day after the irradiation and the lowest value is reached after about seven days. The dose required to give a significant depression lies between 50 and 75 r and it is therefore less radiosensitive than a lymphocyte count, but it provides a much more important indication of the seriousness of the radiation injury. The number of granulocytes does not return to normal for at least two to three weeks, and it is during this period that death from acute radiation sickness occurs. An increase in the number of blood cells is a very good sign, and suggests that recovery will occur. With chronic exposure the fall in granulocytes occurs very slowly, but there is also much less power of recovery than with lymphocytes, and the count may stay permanently low after all exposure to radiation had come to an end.

The restoration of the granulocyte count following single irradiation is brought about by the release of cells held in reserve in the spleen, and in addition reticulocytes are released from the bone-marrow before these have had a chance to develop into the fully differentiated cells. The presence of the so-called immature cells is very typical of radiation damage and about two to four weeks after a severe exposure (depending on the animal used) the number of these cells is greatly in excess of those normally present (Fig. 22). The presence of these immature cells is not neces-

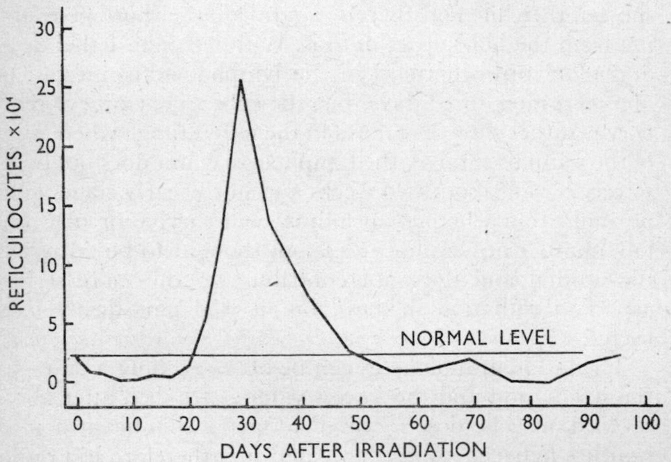

Fig. 22 – Appearance of an excessive number of immature blood cells (reticulocytes) after a severe but not fatal irradiation. (Monkey given 500 r of X-rays.)

sarily beneficial, since they cannot exercise all the functions of the fully differentiated cells and can be harmful to some important organs. This is a typical case of how radiation can upset the fine balance of the whole body and interfere with organs which are themselves radiation-resistant.

The fall in platelets can be observed at about the 100 r level and in general follows that of the granulocytes, except that recovery occurs rather more slowly. The fall in platelets is of the greatest importance, since it is responsible for the haemorrhages which are such a characteristic feature of radiation sickness. Increased fragility of the blood vessels after irradiation is a contributory factor, but the most important cause of haemorrhage after irradiation is the reduction of platelets and the consequent failure of the blood to coagulate. The severity and most common site of these haemorrhages vary from species to species and depend on the dose. Although they are unlikely to be the cause of death following an irradiation with a dose sufficient to kill all the animals (i.e. substantially greater than LD50), the severity of the haemorrhages may often determine whether an animal lives or dies after a dose near the lethal range. A little extra exertion or a small additional injury, such as a cut or abrasion, may greatly affect the severity of the haemorrhage because of the virtual absence of platelets.

The red cells themselves are extremely radiation-resistant, and doses of tens of thousands of roentgen are necessary before any change can be detected in their behaviour. Exposures of the order of those which produce radiation sickness will leave the circulating cells entirely unaffected and allow them to continue their normal function. Since they persist for many months, interference with the formation of their precursors by stopping cell division in the bone-marrow cannot make itself felt for many weeks, by which time normal cell division – as shown by the recovery in the lymphocyte count – will have set in. Nevertheless a diminution in the red blood cells is observed after whole body doses, about one week after irradiation, and continues for about three weeks; it is at a minimum when the lymphocytes and granulocytes are nearly back to normal. The reason for this drop and the general anaemia always found after severe irradiation is the haemorrhages, which often result in serious loss of blood. Chronic irradiation may give rise to protracted anaemia, even though the white cells are normal, because the areas of the bone-marrow in which the red cells are formed have less power of recovery from radiation damage than those producing white cells. With a single dose permanent loss of generative power is generally small and the immediate effects on the blood are due to temporary inhibition of cell division, resulting in a deficiency, followed by release of immature and abnormal cells, which tend to upset some of the many functions for which the blood is responsible. The *status quo* is eventually re-established if the dose has not been too great. Protracted irradiation may effect an irreversible change by permanently reducing the number of blood cells produced.

Loss of weight. The pattern of weight changes following irradiation runs parallel with the blood picture. After a dose of several hundred roentgen all animals immediately begin

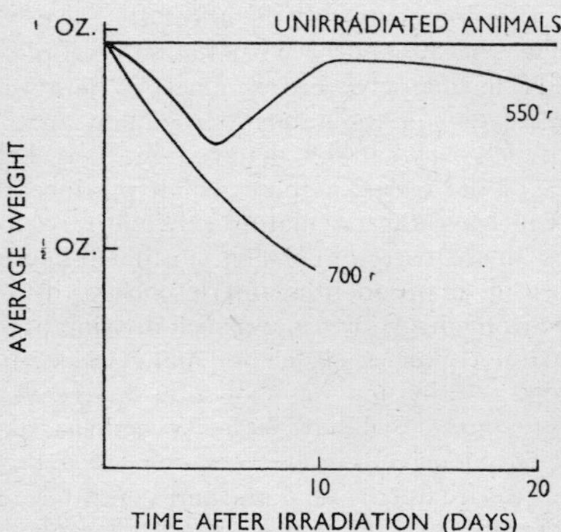

Fig. 23 – Loss of weight of mice after a single dose of radiation. With 700 r all the animals died, and lost weight till death; with 550 r nearly all the animals survived, and their weight returned to normal.

to lose weight (see Fig. 23) because of the general symptoms of severe radiation sickness which lead to a complete loss of appetite and to diarrhoea. Animals which do not survive continue to lose weight until death, but the curve for survivors passes through a minimum, at a time which depends on the species and the severity of the radiation, and then goes up again to that before irradiation. If young animals which are still growing are used, a second weight drop can be observed. This is clearly brought out in Fig. 24,

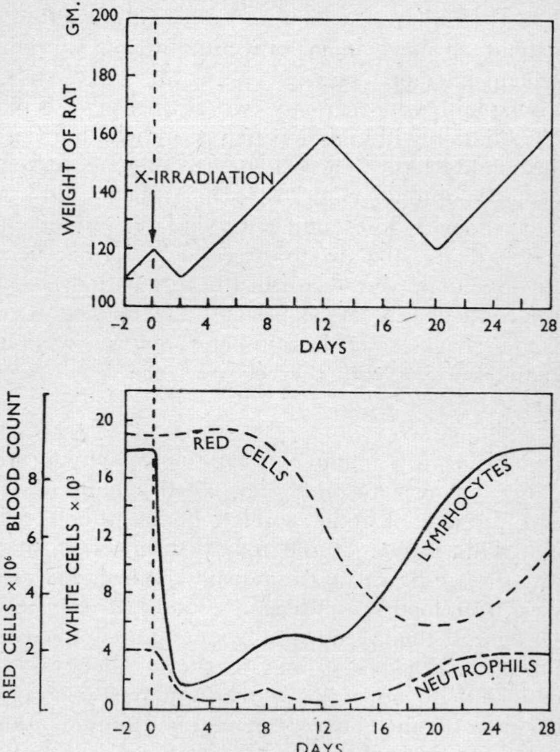

Fig. 24 – Effect of irradiation on weight of young animals (rats) which are still growing. The two periods of weight loss coincide with a drop in the number of white cells and of red cells of the blood respectively.

where it can be seen that the initial weight loss follows the lymphocyte count and is reversed on the general recovery of the animals within the first week. Then suddenly, about two weeks later, a second drop occurs which coincides with the fall in the number of red cells, and this weight loss is a measure of the haemorrhages. If these haemorrhages are very severe because of some additional factors, death will occur at this time. That is, the animal has survived the first shock of the radiation which normally kills at lethal doses, but its platelet shortage has prevented it from surviving the subsequent haemorrhages.

This explains why there are two distinct periods of death after irradiation with a dose which is in the lethal range but not invariably fatal. There is death after about ten days following the initial weight loss – this is the period in which death occurs with doses sufficient to kill all animals – and an occasional death after two to three weeks. In man very little can be done to prevent death in the first period (see p. 84); but these late deaths can be prevented by medical treatment for haemorrhages, since the number of platelets will be going up again, parallel with the recovery of the white cells in general.

Infection. Healthy mammals have the capacity for forming substances, known as antibodies, which combine with and thereby put out of action foreign bodies which enter the system. This is one of the major defences of mammals against disease-producing organisms. When, for example, bacteria from food which has gone bad are absorbed, antibodies against them are made by the animal and will keep the infection in check so long as the invaders are not too virulent and do not damage the host too severely before sufficient antibodies have been made. Immunization consists of stimulating the body to make antibodies against a particular bacterium or virus which is dangerous. This is usually done by injecting the virus in an attenuated form, in which it still stimulates antibody formation but does not produce the symptoms of the disease (compare p. 199). After immunization the body has the antibodies in readiness, or the antibody-forming organs have 'learned' how to make the particular antibody required and can produce it more rapidly the next time. Then when it comes into contact with the invader again the immunized animal is able to combat the dangerous organisms immediately, before they have a chance of becoming established.

One of the most typical symptoms of radiation sickness is the much greater susceptibility to infection. Small and insignificant wounds turn septic after a whole body irradiation and many infections set in spontaneously. The reason for this is twofold; the mucous membranes of the intestine become thin and ulcerated and aided by local haemorrhages the bacteria from the intestine gain access to other parts of the body. This in itself would probably not be sufficient to make the infections as serious as they are, but the body has at the same time lost its capacity to form antibodies. These are probably produced in the blood-forming organs, and interference with them is another aspect of the effect of radiation on the blood. Whether the cells which actually make the antibodies are destroyed and become replaced by new ones, or whether radiation merely temporarily inhibits their protein-synthesizing activity, is not known. However, the dose required before loss in immunity-producing properties is observed is of the order of several hundred roentgen. Shielding part of the blood-forming organs from the radiation prevents the interference with antibody formation, and this must contribute to the great protective effect of excluding parts of the body from irradiation (see p. 75). These infections are a very serious part of radiation sickness, and if not treated can lead to death, but they are not the normal cause of death with doses of radiation in the lethal range.

Effect on reproduction. It is necessary to distinguish between localized irradiation confined to the sex organs, and whole body irradiation. Permanent sterility can be produced by irradiating the ovaries with about 1,000 r; in the male this dose will give only temporary sterility, and permanent destruction of the organs in which the sperms are generated requires several thousand roentgen in most mammals, including man.

Following a whole body irradiation of 400 r or more the male remains fertile for many weeks, but then becomes sterile for a protracted period of several months. Recovery of the reproductive organs takes longer than that of others, and sterility can be said to be the most protracted symptom of radiation sickness. The reason for the delay of about two weeks between irradiation and the diminution in the number of sperms – complete sterility requires a minimum of 400 r and occurs as late as a month after a single dose of radiation – is due to the fact that the mature sperms are very radiation-resistant, so that successful mating is possible by a male who has received a lethal dose and will shortly die. The earlier stages of the germ cells are radiation-sensitive, so that the supply of mature sperms is interrupted by the irradiation. The long delay before fertility occurs again is due to slow recovery of the germ cells coupled with the fact that it takes several weeks for a newly formed germ cell to develop into a mature sperm. Complete recovery occurs in animals and, so far as can be judged from the limited number of 'atomic accidents' and the Japanese casualties, in man also.

Ovarian tissue is much more sensitive and it has been claimed that a whole body irradiation of 150 r has caused permanent sterility in mice. Again the generative cells are the most sensitive, while the fully differentiated ovum is unaffected. Menstruation will therefore continue for a time even after a very heavy dose (with mice two litters can occasionally be got after irradiation before permanent sterility becomes apparent), but will cease for a long period or completely if the dose exceeds the so-called castration level (about 300 r for human beings),* which is however rather variable even within one species.

The skin. In March 1896, only three months after Röntgen published his discovery of X-rays, their destructive action

* The practice of gynaecologists of stimulating fertility by irradiating the ovaries with 175 r is no contradiction of this, since this is a localized exposure as opposed to a whole body dose. Reference is made on p. 125 to the harm which could occur if this form of treatment were carried out widely.

on living matter was revealed by their depilatory action. Irradiation with a few hundred roentgen by all types of rays causes hair to fall out about a week or so later. This is a local effect and the whole body need not be exposed: the part irradiated can be recognized from the loss of hair. This is particularly noticeable following exposure to β-rays, given off by a radioactive substance, since these only penetrate a small fraction of an inch and do not, unless ingested, produce general radiation sickness. Usually the hair growth returns and no permanent damage is left behind with doses of two or three hundred roentgen. This is illustrated by the photographs on Plate 9a, which show a young South Sea Island girl, on whose head had settled radioactive dust released in an American hydrogen bomb trial. A year later the hair had returned to normal. For most human beings more than 500 r permanently damages hair growth and the new hair will be sparse and weaker. Larger irradiations still cause permanent baldness; but for all these changes it is difficult to give a definite threshold dose, since there are remarkable variations not only between species but even from one person to another.

After fairly big doses the appearance of the hair and sometimes also its colour are altered. These changes are permanent, indicating that cells responsible for secreting the pigment or other substances associated with the hair have been permanently destroyed. An effect of this type is shown most markedly in certain strains of black mice, whose hair is turned permanently white after irradiation; all new hairs in the irradiated region are white, and the pigment never returns. Plate 8a shows the greying produced by irradiating a mouse with 800 r of X-rays in a narrow beam. The X-rays are very penetrating and go right through the mouse, so that the white colour occurs on both sides of the animal. Since this dose was confined to a very small volume only, no symptoms of radiation sickness were produced.

The effect of radiation on the skin is extremely well defined, and was used as a means of measuring the dose from X-ray machines before physical methods had been developed. The changes produced depend only on the local dose received, and are independent of radiation to the remainder of the body. Damage to the cells in the skin is not influenced by irradiation of other organs or of other skin at some distance away, and differs very markedly in this respect from irradiation of the blood-forming organs and the associated general symptoms of radiation sickness. Injury follows a general pattern; within a few hours after exposure the affected parts redden temporarily. This effect is usually very mild and sometimes is not observed at all; it wears off after a day or so. More than a week later definite reddening develops and the extent of this so-called erythema varies very much with dose and dose rate. This reddening is an inflammation of the kind which is evoked in damaged tissue by many forms of injury, not only radiation. The skin shows remarkable power of recovery, so that by extending the time over which the dose is given to more than one hour the damage is greatly decreased; as the dose rate decreases, the total dose necessary to produce a certain degree of erythema is increased. This is shown in Table VI, which gives the total dose necessary to produce in man a fixed intensity of skin reddening at two weeks following the irradiations. Narrow beams were used, so that the total areas involved were very small.

TABLE VI

Dose rate	*Total dose necessary*	*Time of irradiation necessary to give dose*
500 r/min.	500 r (this was the chosen reference value)	1 min.
50 r/min.	780 r	15·5 min.
5 r/min.	1,300 r	4 hrs. 20 min.
½ r/min.	2,250 r	75 hrs.

The dose at which definite erythema sets in is usually the same as that causing loss of hair; it is quite temporary and causes little distress. It is often followed by slight changes in pigmentation, and large freckles may be seen. In coloured races loss of pigmentation may occur (see Plate 9b).

With doses exceeding 1,000 r the erythema becomes severe, the skin becomes dark red and blisters are formed. These indicate extensive damage to the skin and can turn into extremely unpleasant running sores which take months to heal and leave bad scars. In radiation treatment of deep-seated cancers the dose tolerated by skin without producing severe erythema is often the limiting factor. Accidental irradiation and contact with radioisotopes have given rise to severe skin damage, which clears up quite quickly if the exposure is not repeated. Plate 9b shows the feet of a native from the Marshall Islands, which were contaminated by radioactive fall-out. Some months later they were completely healed.

The effect on the skin of long-term irradiation, such as exposure of their hands by the early radiologists, is much more serious. A complex process of damage followed by periods of repair often results in overgrowth and causes the skin to dry up. Gradually and insidiously the fingers become stiff. Once this has occurred recovery becomes impossible, and even if all further exposure to radiation is then avoided the affected parts will not improve and may continue to deteriorate. Typical deformities following prolonged local exposure to large doses, which did not produce radiation sickness since only a part of the body was exposed, are shown in Plate 8b.

The first warning that irreversible damage is being done to the skin by irradiation over long periods is a change in the ridges of the finger-tips. This test can be made very sensitive by taking finger-prints which immediately reveal the flattening or disappearance of ridges (see Plate 10a). As the skin is damaged it is replaced, and even when the skin peels off the fingers the identical finger-print pattern is re-established. With chronic radiation a time arrives when the repair process fails to produce an exact copy and the new pattern remains permanently. Even today many radio-therapists and surgeons, who take reasonable precautions, reveal their profession by their finger-tips; certainly the surgeon who inserts radium needles cannot fail to expose his fingers and must watch the symptoms most carefully, for radiation damage may affect the agility of his fingers on which his skill depends.

Cataract. One of the most serious of the non-fatal consequences of irradiation is the clouding over of the lens of the eye. This is known as cataract formation, and can lead to total blindness, although frequently vision is only impaired. There is a long latent period, and five to ten years may elapse between irradiation and the appearance of symptoms. The most important factor is the irradiation of the eye itself, and exposure of the rest of the body is not important. In many respects the irradiation effects of the eye follow closely those of the skin. Dose rate is more important than total dose, and a single heavy dose is the most effective for inducing cataracts. About 400 to 500 r of X- or γ-rays are needed, and for all practical purposes it is not therefore a hazard. Some of the seriously affected victims of the atom bomb explosions in Japan who survived a big dose later developed cataracts; in general, the threshold dose for serious cataract is close to the acute lethal (LD50) dose for whole body irradiation.

Radiations giving rise to densely ionizing tracks, such as fast neutrons, are generally more effective in inducing all types of radiation injuries than X- and γ-rays (see p. 206), but they are exceptionally more effective in producing cataract. Thus the neutron dose necessary for cataract lies well below the LD50 for whole body irradiation. This was first indicated in 1948, when several cases were found in physicists who had been exposed to neutrons from a cyclotron. The greatest danger comes probably from accidental exposure to β-ray-emitting isotopes, whose radiations do not penetrate and do not therefore produce whole body effects; fall-out from bombs is an obvious source.

CHAPTER 4

THE SINS OF THE FATHERS

ONE of the most awful consequences of exposure to ionizing radiations is the effect it may have on future generations. This may come about as a result of irradiation of a mother carrying her child or from damage to the germ cells before fertilization, when it is known as genetic damage. In either case doses which are sufficient to bring about these effects in an appreciable proportion of the children are considerably below those necessary to produce any symptoms of radiation sickness in the parents. In this respect radiation injury is much more insidious and dangerous to the community as a whole than most poisons, and is the aspect of radiation damage which causes the greatest concern. Until recently it was believed that only radiations could produce these long-delayed effects, but chemicals of a class described in Chapter 11 are now known to simulate the action of radiations.

IRRADIATION *in utero*

The primitive embryonic cell known as the zygote which is formed after the entry of the sperm into the ovum is very sensitive to radiation. For example, 80 per cent of mice exposed to 200 r of X-rays within the first five days after conception fail to give birth. Smaller doses give rise to a lower incidence of prenatal death, but an appreciable reduction in the average litter size has been observed with 50 r.

At first the embryo grows by cell division without differentiation and becomes firmly implanted in the wall of the uterus; this requires about eight days in human beings and five days in mice. Then differentiation begins and the individual organs and limbs are formed; the embryo takes shape. During this period it is in the greatest danger. Now radiation no longer kills; the damaged embryo is not reabsorbed or aborted but proceeds to a live birth which is abnormal. These malformations can be very great, so as to give horrible and distressing monsters, which are, however, quite capable of living for a time. The incidence is particularly high in the early stages of active development of the embryo (see Fig. 25). The malformations can be of almost

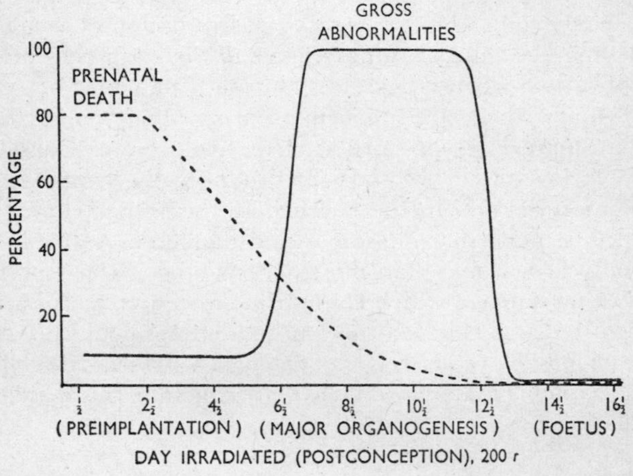

Fig. 25 – Effect of 200 r on mouse embryo; the irradiations were carried out at different times after conception.

every kind, ranging from anatomical, such as cleft palate, short limbs, fusion of ribs, etc., to effects on the central nervous system which reduce intelligence and co-ordination. Often one newborn animal has several abnormalities (see Plates 10b and 11). The type of deformity most likely to be produced depends upon the exact time of irradiation in relation to the age of the embryo. There is a time during the period of embryonic development when many of the abnormalities produced are of such a character as to make it impossible for the newborn animals to survive. In most cases, however, these monsters live. A dose of 200 r at the most sensitive stage will produce gross abnormalities in every offspring. With lower doses the incidence will be less, and some kinds of malformations are not produced at all with less than 50 r. But as little as 25 r can produce certain kinds of deformities, particularly those involving the brain without producing any symptoms in the mother, and even a blood count might not show that an exposure to radiation has occurred.

The period of major organ production is over after about three months in human beings, and the foetus then develops its finer aspects and generally grows and develops. Exposure to doses insufficient to produce severe radiation sickness in the mother no longer produces gross deformities (see Fig. 25) which can be recognized in small experimental animals, but the absence of striking changes in the newborn does not mean that the irradiation has been without harm. The general effect is less obvious but none the less serious, and irradiation at the later stages of pregnancy results in very marked growth reduction, giving small babies which develop into smaller adults. Their life-span is reduced and their reproductive organs are often affected so that they grow up sterile. Damage to the brain and eyes was found a few weeks after birth in all cases which had been irradiated in the foetal stage with 200 r, and there is a significant incidence after 100 r. Since only gross disorders of the brain can be detected in experimental animals it seems likely that much smaller doses will give effects which are serious in man.

Although the manner in which the radiation injury manifests itself depends very much on the stage of development of the embryo, it is highly sensitive at all times. These effects are thought to be the result of the irradiation of the embryo or foetus itself, and changes produced in the womb probably do not play an important part. Since many of the abnormalities can be produced with doses which do not give radiation sickness it seems unlikely that a general effect of radiation on the health of the mother is involved. The detailed picture of the influence of radiation on prenatal development has been obtained from studies with animals. Unhappily, sufficient human cases are known to make it certain that the same pattern also occurs in man, and we can confidently superimpose a human time scale on the mouse data shown in Fig. 25. Some of our information is derived from the survivors of the atom bombs in Japan; the children from women who were pregnant and exposed to irradiation at Nagasaki and Hiroshima are on an average shorter and lighter and have smaller heads, indicating an underdeveloped brain. Some show severe mental deficiencies, while others were unable to speak normally at five years old. Most of our knowledge comes from expectant mothers who were irradiated for therapeutic or diagnostic reasons. Many cases are described in the medical literature of abnormalities following exposure of the embryo; most of these arose twenty or thirty years ago at a time when radiologists did not know of the great radiosensitivity of the foetus or believed that any harmful effects would lead to abortion or still births, and that the embryonic abnormalities would not give rise to deformed children. This view is quite wrong. A detailed survey showed that where a mother received several hundred roentgen within the first two months after implantation of the embryo, severe maldevelopment was observed in every child, a high proportion of whom lived for many years. In these cases the mother had received the high doses to the abdomen as a treatment for cancer. A much smaller proportion of malformed children were born when the mother was irradiated during the last three months of pregnancy.

The local dose received in an ordinary diagnostic X-ray examination depends largely on the site which is examined. In chest X-rays it will be much less than 1 r, but when the pelvis is studied doses of up to 10 r may be necessary, and it may happen that considerably higher doses are given inadvertently or because the machine is not running correctly. There are some diagnostic procedures where the local dose received may run up to as much as 100 r, and there can be no question about their dangers to the embryo. In good medical practice irradiation of pregnant women has long been avoided, and where exposure of the pelvis is essential for therapeutic purposes and cannot be postponed the physician should seriously consider terminating the pregnancy. The embryo is, however, at its most sensitive (see Fig. 25) during the period of most active organ development, which lasts from the second to the sixth week after conception. During part of this time at least pregnancy may be entirely unsuspected and the physician may go ahead with an extensive diagnostic investigation or even with radiation treatment. Attention has been drawn to this very serious problem by the American biologists Dr and Mrs Russell, to whom we owe most of our detailed information about the radiation hazards to the embryo and foetus *in utero*. They have suggested a routine to be followed for the irradiation of the pelvic regions of women of childbearing age which would overcome this danger.

THE HEREDITY MECHANISM

We have seen how irradiation can affect the unborn child, but it can reach even further and affect the children of parents not yet born. The very existence of a genetic injury will be quite unknown until it becomes revealed in future generations, and it may remain hidden for a number of generations.

The modern theory of inheritance ranks amongst the greatest of scientific achievements, and scant justice can be done to it in a brief summary. However, the salient features are simple and far-reaching and suffice to show how atomic radiations can affect the make-up of our whole species for all time. The interplay of genetic and external factors makes us what we are; we inherit a number of characteristics which are moulded by environment into the complete personality. One way of finding out about the relative contribution of heredity and environment is the study of identical twins. Children derived from the same egg which splits into two embryos during cleavage have identical genetic constitutions, and differences between these twins must have been caused by external factors. Many physical characteristics such as eye colour or blood type are inherited, but with regard to intellectual achievement the position is more complex. Differences there will be between identical twins, yet heredity enters into the picture; it probably determines the upper limits which can be attained, while environment determines the use made of what is there. We inherit certain physiological states which outside influences develop and guide into final characteristics which may be entirely different. These acquired properties cannot be transmitted to future generations; children will not be born with characteristics acquired by their parents – they may have the same basic genetic make-up so that under identical environmental conditions the same characteristics may again appear. Take them into different surroundings and their inherent properties will be moulded into other directions. The individual known as the 'phenotype' is the product of environment acting on the basic 'genotype' which is inherited.

The laws of inheritance were discovered by the abbot of a small monastery near Vienna, Gregor Mendel, who spent much of his spare time cultivating the edible and the sweet pea. By comparing the characteristics of hybrids he was led to the idea that inherited properties are transmitted from parents to offspring by entities called genes which are segregated in the germ cells according to well defined rules. The genes determine the type of organ which is produced, but do not themselves play a part in its synthesis. For example, the gene responsible for the blue colour of eyes does not itself make the pigment but ensures that during growth the animal develops the right biochemical equipment which makes the blue pigment. We now know that the genes form part of the chromosomes and that each gene occupies a specific position in its chromosome. In the fertilized ovum there are two sets of chromosomes, one derived from the egg and the other from the sperm. All cells in the developed animal contain an identical set of chromosomes derived in equal part from the chromosomes of the mother and of the father. The child therefore receives from its two parents two sets of genes, one of which is the counterpart of the other. The two genes which determine the same characteristics are known as alleles, but these do not in general express themselves in the development to the same extent.

Eye colour illustrates the dominance of one over the other allele. A child may have the gene 'B' for brown eyes and its allele 'b' which gives blue eyes from the other parent. Its eye colour will be brown because 'B' is dominant over 'b'; to have blue eyes its chromosome constitution must be 'bb'. Now brown-eyed people of the constitution 'BB' or 'Bb' look alike, since 'B' is 'dominant', and we cannot tell their genetic constitution until we have seen their offspring. The mixing of genes is brought about as follows: the germ cells contain only one set of chromosomes, which is produced in a complicated process known as meiosis in which the two chromosomes are mixed and come out in different cells with one set of chromosomes each, neither of which has the same set of genes as either of the parent's chromosomes. This reductive division is illustrated in Fig. 10 and the consequent reshuffling of genes is a most effective mechanism for producing individuals who differ in their genetic make-up and is responsible for the difference between animals of the same species and between parents and children. To return to the eye colour problem. Both 'BB' and 'Bb' individuals have brown eyes, and we have no way of finding out by inspection which is which, but they differ in that the former can have only offspring with brown eyes, since his sperm cells must all contain the 'B' gene. The 'Bb' adult can beget blue-eyed children if the other parent is either 'Bb' or 'bb'.

The important factor is that we all carry many 'recessive' genes, the presence of which does not make itself felt and can be recognized only in subsequent generations. Many mental diseases are associated with recessive genes and will therefore produce defective children only when both parents have the same recessive genes. More than 500 defects and diseases of man have been shown to be hereditary, and many more may in fact be so. Two to three per cent of the world's population suffer from severe hereditary afflictions, and all of us carry some recessive genes which an unfortunate mating could reveal in a child.

Mutations. Genes are not completely stable; they undergo changes known as mutations. The gene may be altered in such a way that it causes a different structure to be made (e.g. a different eye colour). Alternatively the mutation can result in the loss of a gene, so that the property determined by it is no longer formed. If the gene determining the eye colour is lost, then albino offspring will be born. The important point about mutations is that they are, in general, unfavourable. Only very rarely does a mutation improve the species; much more frequently it introduces a point of weakness. A single mutation can never change a genotype capable of average intellectual attainment only into one capable of genius, since many genes are involved in giving outstanding ability and it is most unlikely that all these will mutate at the same time. On the other hand, mutation of a single gene by impairing one particular function can give rise to a mentally deficient genotype. The ability to produce necessary hormones such as insulin, or other vital substances such as those which cause blood to clot, is genetically determined, and a mutation can give rise to a haemophilic or a diabetic. There is much scope for harmful mutations, while those which are favourable, for example by increasing resistance to disease, come about only through a rare concurrence of circumstances.

For the same reason most of the recessive genes we carry would, if they came to the fore, produce unfavourable characteristics. This is why geneticists speak of 'man's genetic load', meaning the threat held over all our heads by our hidden or recessive genes. Mutations occur at a very low rate in all animals without any apparent external cause, and they are then referred to as spontaneous. The number of genes in an animal is not known, but is believed to exceed 10,000 in the more complex organisms. Although the chance of a mutation occurring in a particular gene is very small, the possibility of a mutation in any one of all the genes is

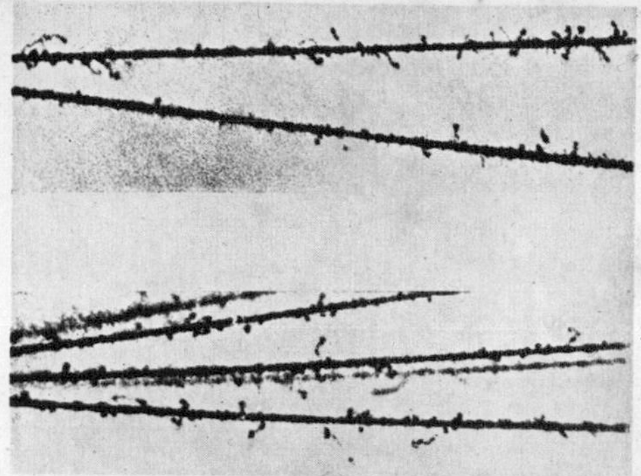

a. Cloud chamber tracks of α-particles. The spurs on the outside of the tracks are the δ-rays, some of which have quite a considerable range.

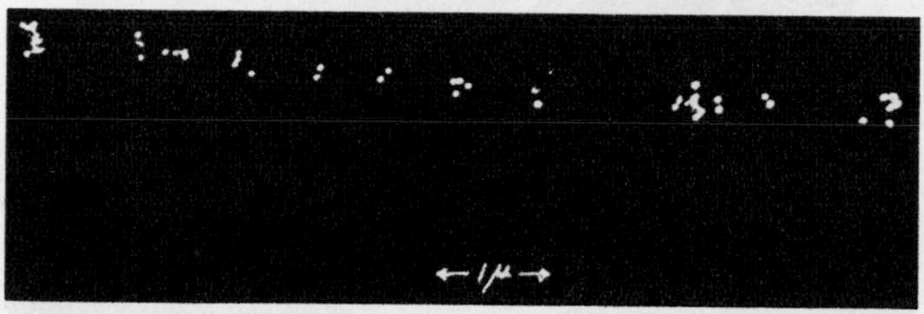

b. Cloud chamber track of a 1 MeV electron, which shows that the ionizations occur in clusters.

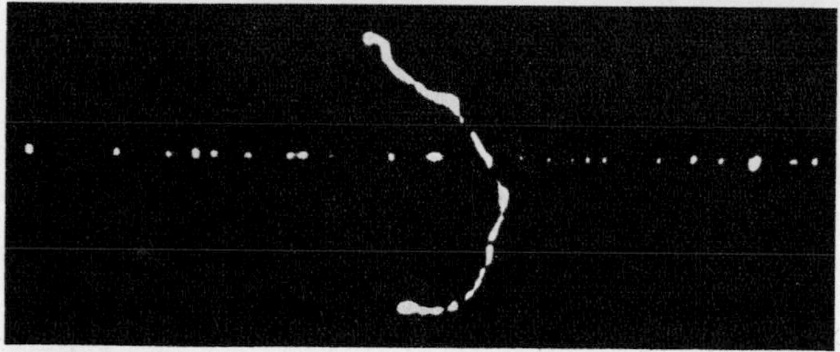

c. Cloud chamber tracks of a fast electron (*circa* 200 kV) crossed by a dense track from a slow electron (*circa* 20 kV); at this low energy the track is bent because of scattering.

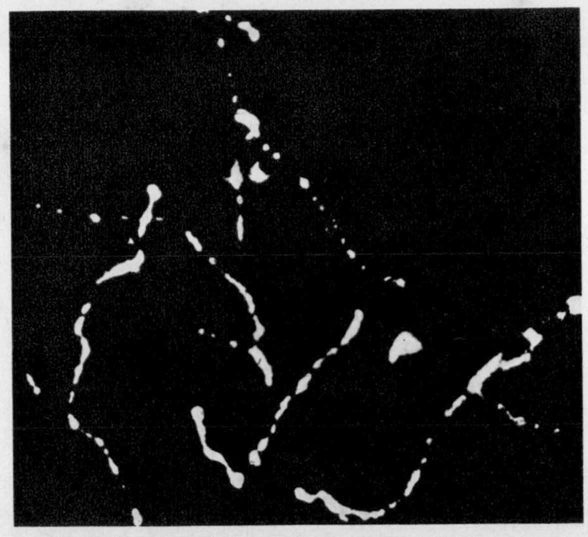

a. Cloud chamber photograph of the electrons produced by irradiation with X-rays from a 200 kV therapy set.

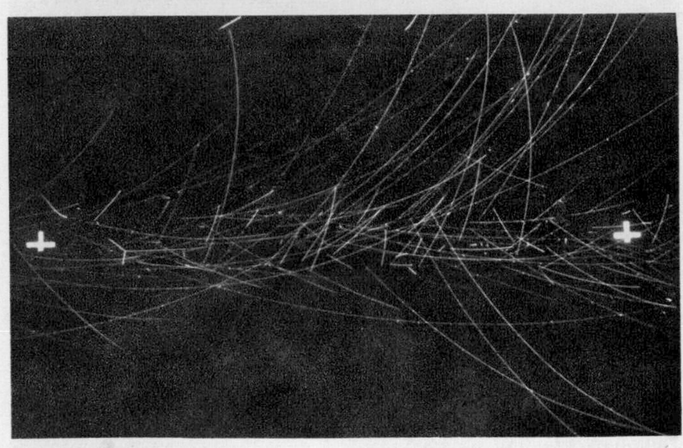

b. Tracks in a cloud chamber of high energy protons produced when a neutron beam traverses a hydrogen-filled cloud chamber. (The tracks are curved owing to the presence of a magnetic field.)

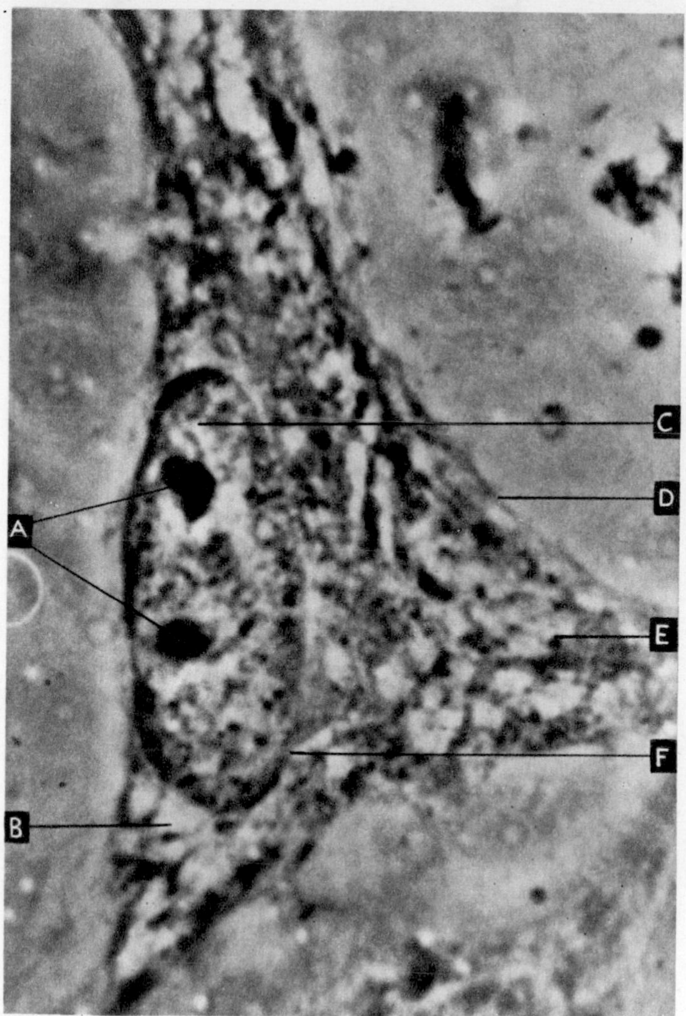

Photomicrograph of a mammalian cell showing presence of the various cell constituents which are represented diagrammatically in Fig. 9. A. Nucleolus, B. Mitochondria, C. Nucleus, D. Cell membrane, E. Fat globule, F. Nuclear membrane.

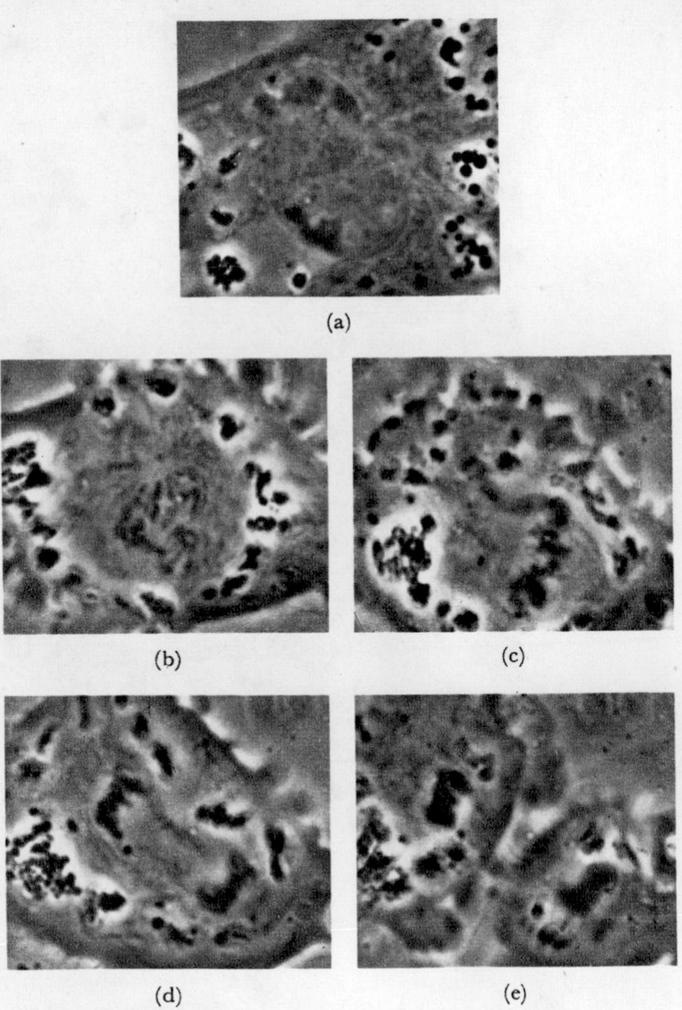

Cell division in tissue culture; stills from a film taken through the phase contrast microscope of a living cell. (a) Early prophase (time zero); (b) prophase (18 min. later); (c) metaphase (35 min. later); (d) anaphase (50 min. later); (e) telophase (59 min. later). Compare with photographs opposite, which show the details more clearly.

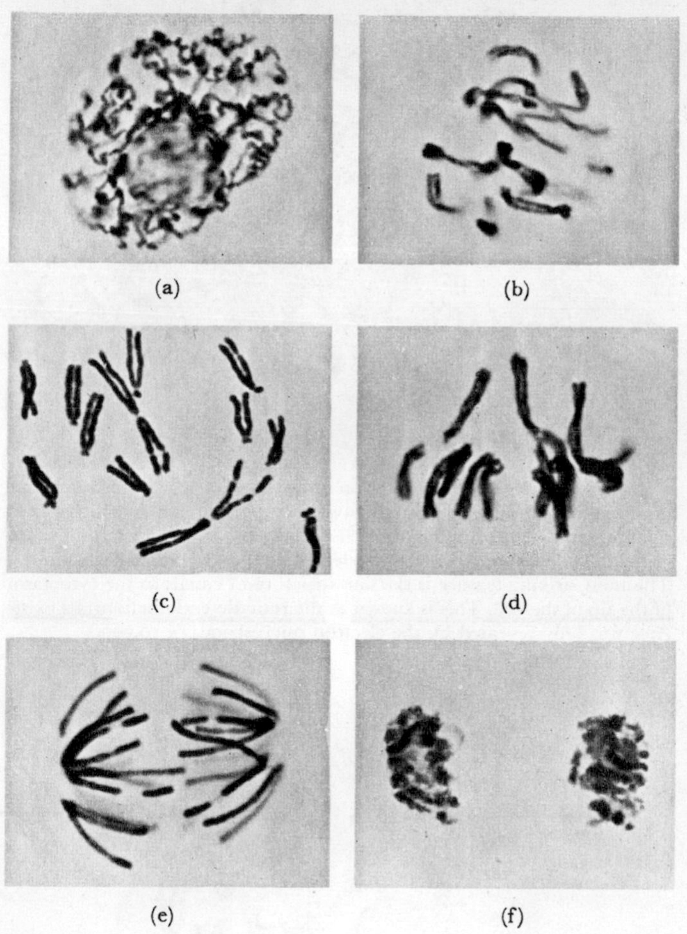

(a) (b) (c) (d) (e) (f)

The mitotic cycle of cells from *vicia faba* (bean shoots). The fine detail is only revealed by staining the cells with a dye, and this series of photographs represents a reconstructed cell cycle, since each is derived from a different cell which is dead at the time the photograph is taken. (a) Early prophase; (b) late prophase; (c) metaphase; (d) metaphase, side view; (e) anaphase; (f) telophase.

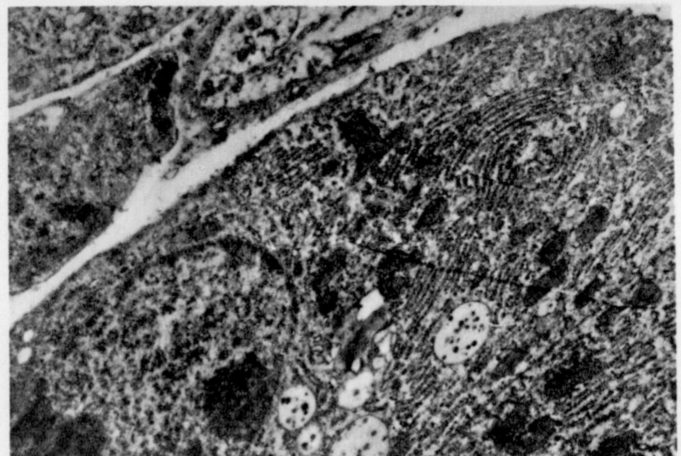

a. Photograph taken in the electron microscope of a cell of a mammary gland. The high magnification allows only part of the cell to be seen; the membranes surrounding the cell and the nucleus (which is shown in part in the left hand corner) can clearly be seen as complex structures. The most striking feature is the fine structure of canals in the cytoplasm of the tip of the cell. This is known as the reticulo endothelium; its existence was only revealed by the electron microscope. (× 10,000.)

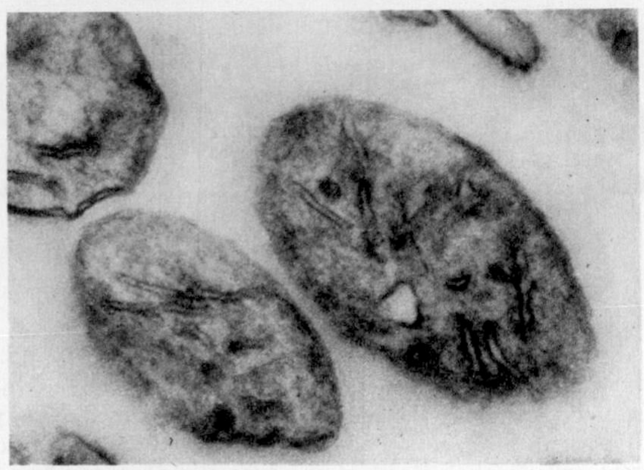

b. Electron microscope photograph of mitochondria; the existence of these bodies in the cytoplasm was recognized in the optical microscope, which could not, however, reveal the fine structure seen here. The mitochondria are surrounded by a series of membranes which cannot be seen in the reproduction. (× 10,000.)

a. Different types of chromosome abnormalities produced by irradiation. *Left:* Star formed by chromatid exchange. *Centre:* Bridges formed between chromosome sets together with an acentric fragment. *Right*: Micronucleus formed from chromosome fragments after cell division is complete. This is in addition to the two new sister cells now in the resting stage.

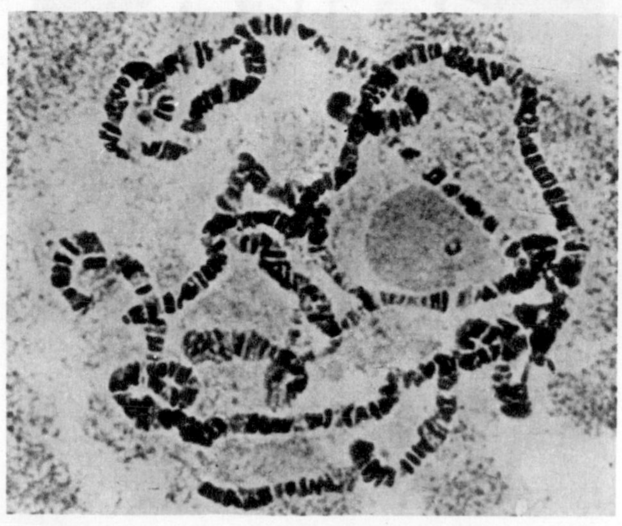

b. Giant chromosome of the salivary gland of the fruit fly (*Drosophila*) showing characteristic banded structure. The position of many different genes along this chromosome has been determined.

a. Mouse showing patch of white hair following irradiation with a narrow beam of X-rays. A similar patch of white was produced on the other side of the animal, marking the exit of the beam.

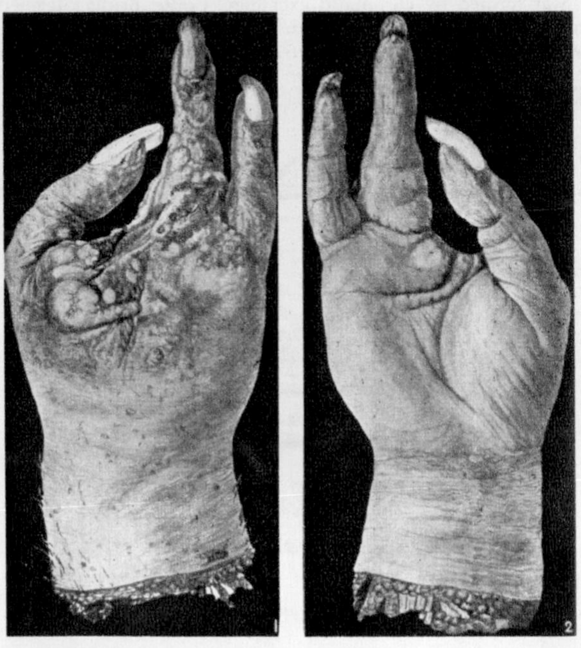

b. Right hand of a pioneer radiologist. The first injury was seen in 1899; the hand was amputated in 1932 and death from disseminated cancer occurred in 1933.

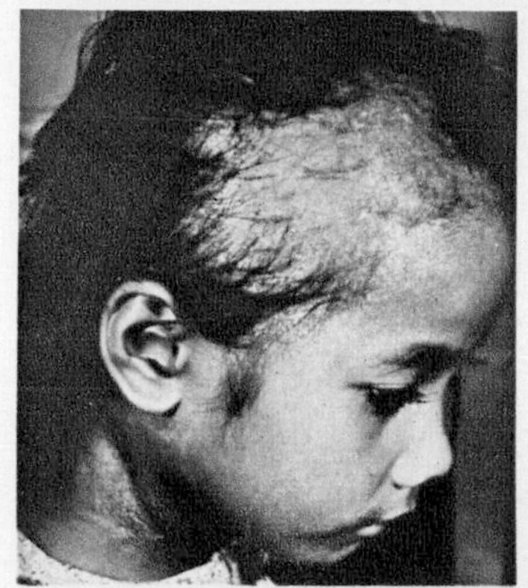
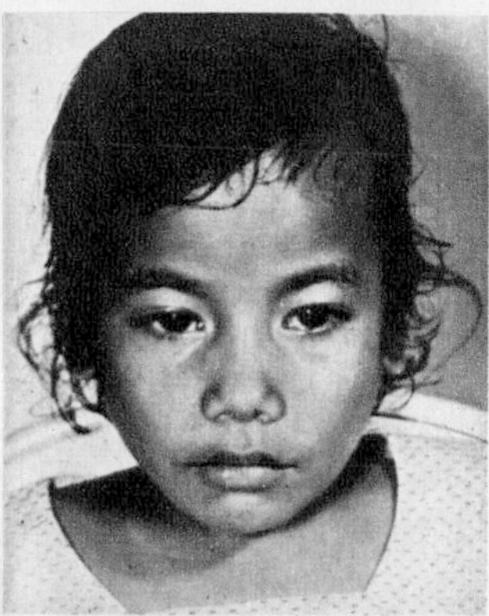

a. Photograph of seven-year-old South Sea Island girl exposed to radioactive fall-out. *Left:* Loss of hair 28 days after explosion. *Right:* Complete regrowth six months later.

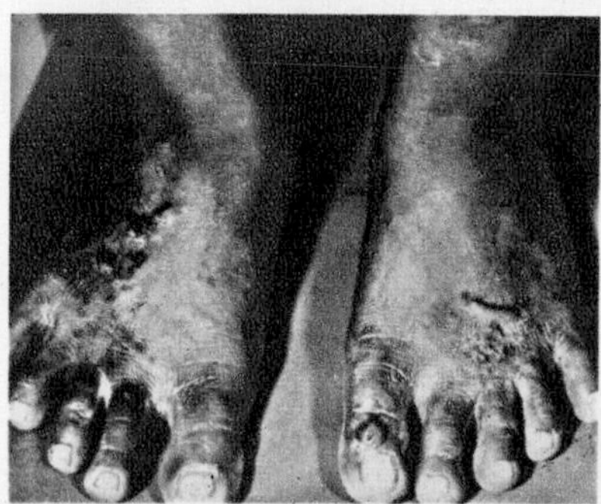
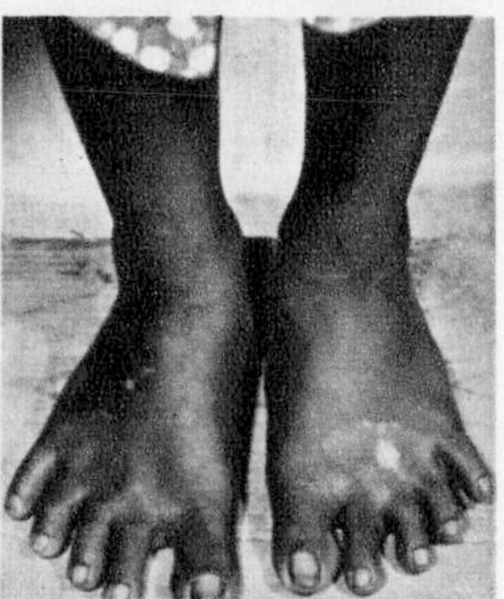

b. Feet of South Sea Islander irradiated by bomb fall-out. *Left:* 28 days after exposure, areas of the skin have lost pigment and appear white. *Right:* Six months later all the injuries have healed but there is permanent loss of pigment at those places where burns were most severe.

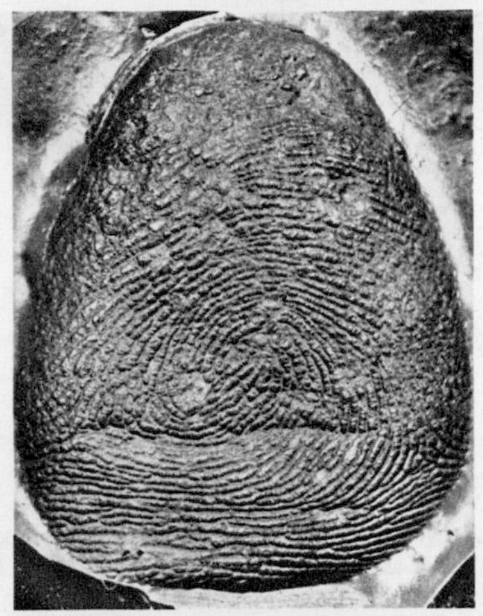

a. Permanent damage to the ridges of the fingers of a surgeon after handling radium needles for many years.

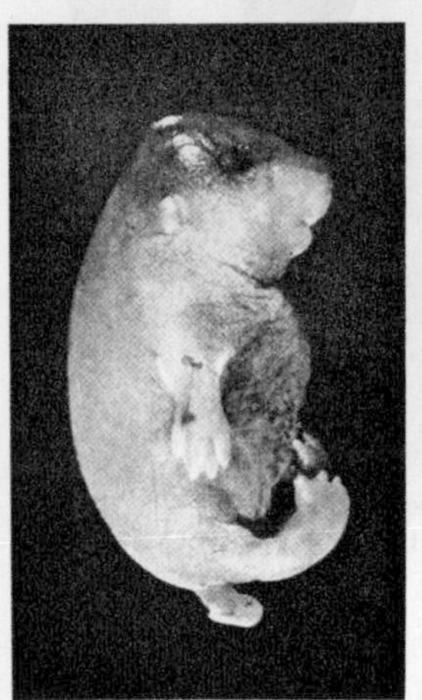

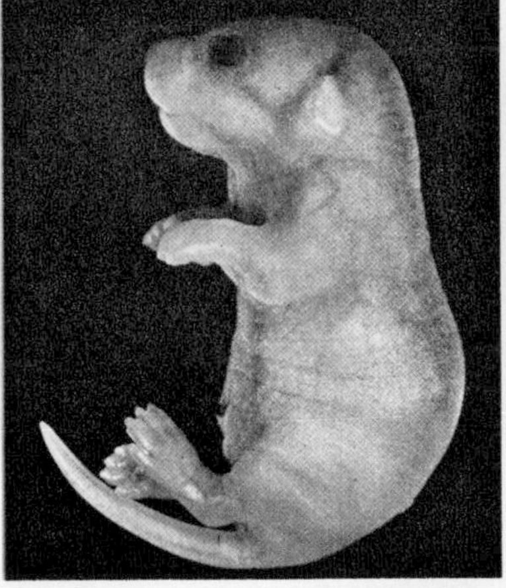

b. Newborn mouse which had been irradiated ten and a half days post-conception with 300 *r left*, compared with control newborn *right*. Note size reduction and change in body shape; rigid elbow joint; rotated heels; abnormal feet; short, coiled tail; microcephaly; bulging of brain through defective cranium; open eyelids (abnormal for newborn mouse).

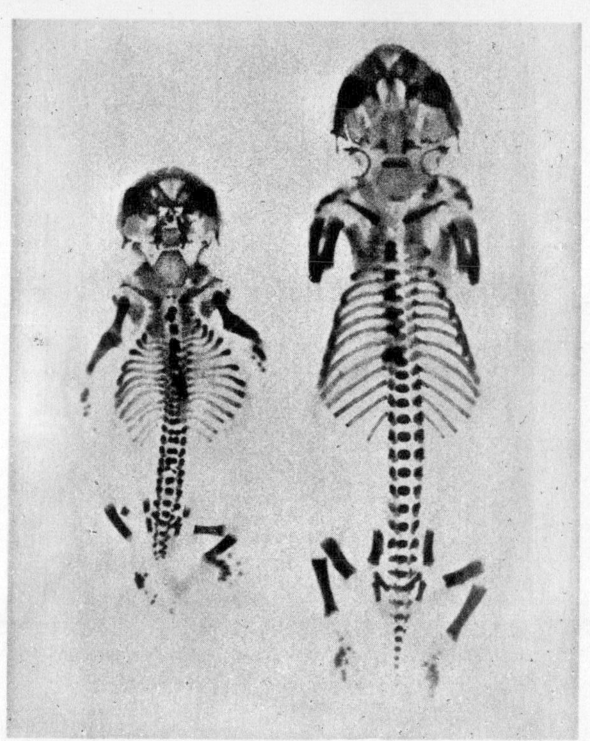

Skeletal comparison of mice similar to those shown in Plate 10b. Note that hardly a single bone in the animal on the left is normal. The following changes are among the more obvious ones: cleft palate; reduced scapula; wide flat thorax with angulated and broken ribs and a reduced number of sternebrae. Note that this very abnormal type of animal is born rather than aborted or resorbed. The postfertilization day (10½) on which this mouse was irradiated corresponds to four weeks after conception in human gestation. By that time, few women realize that they are pregnant and the embryo may thus be unknowingly exposed to radiation. Although 300 *r* was used to produce the extremely abnormal mouse illustrated above, 25 *r* can cause detectable changes if administered at critical developmental stages (see Chap. 4).

a. Ears from different barley mutants produced by irradiation. *Left to right:* Ears of Bonus barley (control), erectoides 32, erectoides 23, giant 1, calcaroides.

b. Experimental plot on which irradiated seeds of barley are grown. The arrows show clearly distinguishable mutations resulting in a reduced formation of the green pigment chlorophyll. (1) xantha (yellow); (2) alboxantha (white tip, yellow base); (3) albina (white); (4) albina, with reduced leaves; (5) albina; (6) viridis (light green).

Visible mutations produced in the fruit fly by irradiation and chemicals (× 12). *Above*. Normal fly. *Below, left*. Bent wings and smaller eye are clearly visible changes. *Below, right*. Darker colour and smaller size.

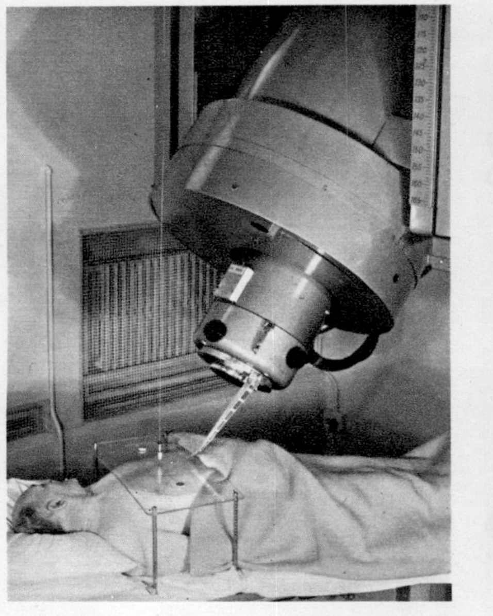

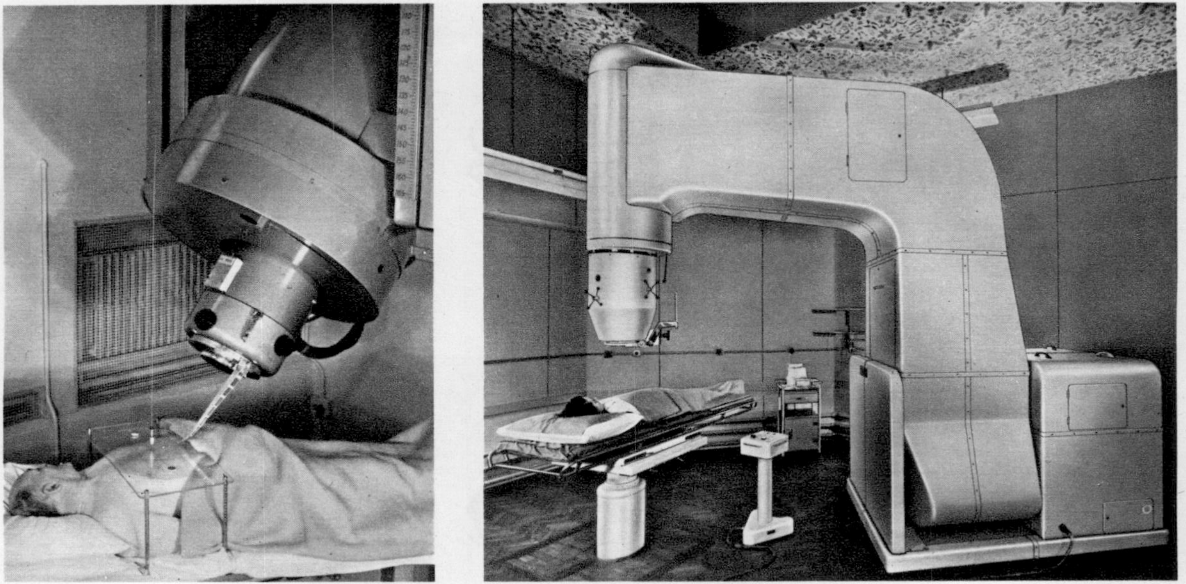

Modern machines for the treatment of deep-seated tumours. *Left:* Two million volt van de Graaf X-ray generator. (Royal Marsden Hospital.) *Right:* Four million volt linear accelerator.

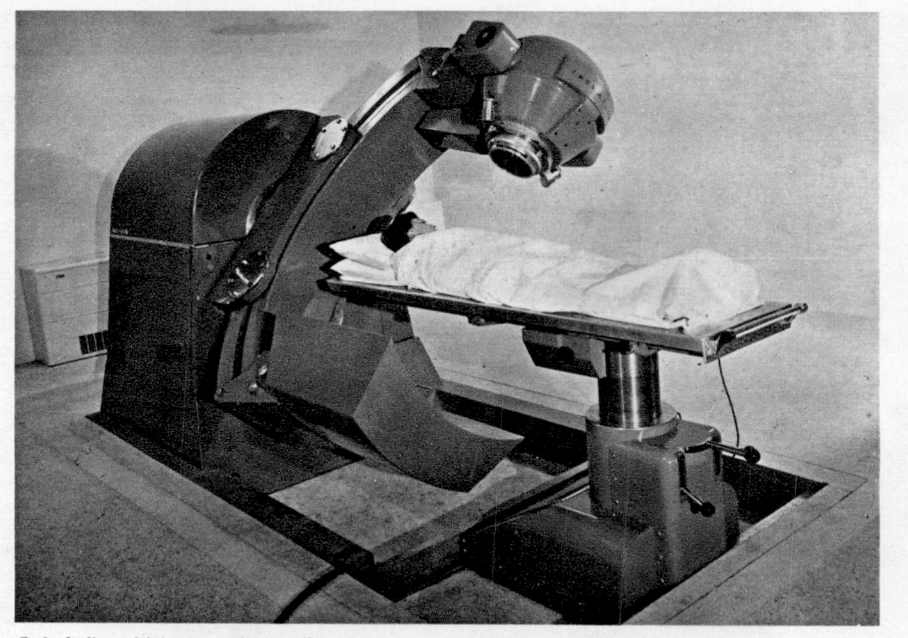

Cobalt 'bomb' (γ-rays given off by large quantity of radioactive cobalt 60). This is situated in the head, which can be rotated round the patient.

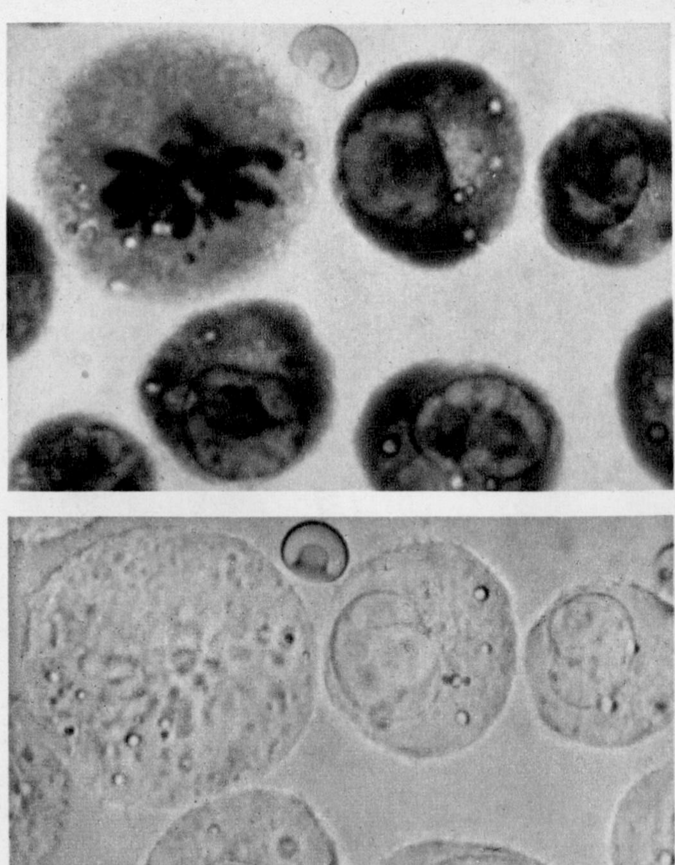

Fresh ascites cells, squashed to a thickness of about 7μ, taken with an ultraviolet microscope (× 1500); *Above,* taken with light of 2,573 Å wavelength, which is more strongly absorbed by nucleic acids than by proteins – the location of the nucleic acids, present in both cytoplasm and nucleus, is shown by the dark portions: chromosomes, rich in nucleic acids, can be seen in the two dividing cells in the top corners; *Below,* taken with a light of 3123 Å wavelength – at this wavelength neither nucleic acids nor proteins absorb, the details are revealed by the scattering of light due to variations in density.

considerable. In wild life there is a continual weeding out of unfavourable mutations by natural selection. As a result harmful changes are not perpetuated for ever, since the animals carrying them will not survive in a fiercely competitive society. The genetic load is kept constant under these conditions because in time elimination of unfavourable genes by selection must become equal to the new genes introduced by mutation. Under these conditions mutations favour the species, since they make evolution possible by selecting out the very rare favourable mutations. Civilized man is different; he has adapted the environment to his needs, and greatly reduced the selection pressure. For example, in 1927 there were in Denmark 12 diabetics to every 10,000 of the population,* while in 1946, only twenty years later, this number had increased three and a half times to 43 per 10,000. Much of this increase can be attributed to an increase in the load of the recessive gene favouring diabetes, which has occurred because insulin reduced the natural selection pressure against diabetics. This situation is not necessarily bad for the population, since in a civilized society many handicaps are no longer serious and do not prevent the leading of a full and valuable life. In fact the people most valuable to a modern society are probably not at all adapted to primitive life where selection pressure would work against them. The fear sometimes expressed that the human population must degenerate and eventually collapse because of reduced fitness is probably unfounded. Man can carry the increased load because he controls his environment, but it is a precarious balance which must not be upset.

If the number of new mutations becomes greater than the selection pressure which eliminates unfit genotypes, then the establishment of a new equilibrium may be very painful in a modern society. In the past only those members of the population actually carrying the genetic load were affected, but in a welfare state genetic unbalance means that the

* These figures were obtained from a survey of all Danish physicians to assess the demand for insulin.

total number of unfit people will increase and require more hospitals, more asylums, doctors, nurses, and drugs. Such a situation could rapidly bring about the economic collapse of states whose governments are pledged to extensive social services, which is the trend of twentieth-century culture. The resulting anarchy would no doubt re-establish genetic equilibrium, but the price of achieving the increased selection pressure would be high. These are no fantasies, and the concern of geneticists about exposure of large numbers of people to very small doses of radiation is fully justified. The danger to the individual and his children is very indirect, but is present none the less. The famous geneticist H. J. Muller, who in 1928 discovered that radiations could induce mutations, said at the Conference on Nuclear Energy organized by UNO at Geneva, 1955, 'Man's own reproductive material is his most invaluable, irretrievable possession. It is already subject to an amount of variation which in relation to his present reproductive practices borders on the excessive. Under these circumstances man's first concern in dealing with radiation must be his own protection.' The science of genetics is relatively new, and progress inevitably requires time; no 'crash-through programme' can provide answers, since nature determines the timetable of these experiments. We can consider ourselves fortunate that the harnessing of nuclear energy with its associated radiation dangers came at a time when geneticists were in a position to point out the danger from doses well below those which can be tolerated if only radiation sickness and the dangers of producing cancer are considered. The insidious gradualness of the changes and the inevitability of their long-term effect make it impossible to wait for actual human experience before delineating the genetic risk. The dangers of radiation to large sections of the population must be anticipated; once they have shown themselves in the population irretrievable damage has been done. Speculation on how mankind's greatest technological blessing – unlimited energy from the atom – could in time have brought about the end of civilization if the discoveries of physics and biology had been out of step, fortunately belongs to the realm of science fiction – or at least we still have time to make sure that it does.

HOW DO ATOMIC RADIATIONS PRODUCE MUTATIONS?

Only irradiation of the germ cells, the ovum, the sperm, or the cells of the organs in which they are formed, can give rise to mutations. Although all the cells of the body carry all the genes they fulfil their genetic function only in the germ cells. If a mutation is produced by irradiation of the germinal tissue the damage is not confined to the immature germ cells then being formed, but all subsequent sperms or ova produced by the affected cell will carry the mutation. A mutation produced at a time when the germ cells are fully differentiated (i.e. into the mature sperm) is not so harmful, since this mutation will persist only if the actual cell involved gives rise to a fertilized egg.

Since the genes are carried by the chromosomes it is not surprising that some chromosome abnormalities produced by irradiation (see p. 55) should find expression also as mutations. If the damage to the chromosomes is too severe, the cell will die and no mutations can occur. Occasionally the abnormality does not prevent the cell from dividing, when daughter cells will be produced, each of which carries the abnormality. This in itself can be considered a mutation, since the anatomical change of the chromosome is perpetuated and will occur in offspring according to Mendelian laws. But much more important is it that the genes carried by the damaged part of the chromosome will be affected so that other genetic factors will be altered. By comparing the site of the chromosome aberration with the genetic change produced, the position of the different genes along the chromosomes has been determined, and maps have been produced of the position of many of the different genes. Most of the work has been done with the chromosomes of salivary glands of fruit-flies (usually *Drosophila melanogaster*).

These are freaks in so far as they are much larger than all other chromosomes because a great number of them are laid down in parallel. Much fine detail can be seen (see Plate 7b); the different bands are characteristic and experienced workers can immediately detect a change in any one of them. Apart from the fact that the cells conveniently magnify them, these chromosomes are completely representative of the fly and are identical with those from the fertilized egg from which the fly is hatched. Any abnormalities seen will be handed on in the ordinary way to future generations. The possession of these remarkable chromosomes, coupled with the fact that the flies breed rapidly and can be kept in very large numbers, has made them the material chosen by many geneticists. We know much more about their genetic make-up than that of any mammal, including man.

Gene changes called point-mutations, which are not associated with any visible structural alteration of the chromosome and which cannot be detected by microscopic examination, are more common than those which can actually be seen in the chromosome. They are brought about by changes in the material of which the genes are composed. The size and shape of a gene are not known, but it is thought that their function is associated with a macromolecule belonging to the class of nucleoproteins (see p. 216). In a number of ways genes and viruses are related; both are very large molecules containing nucleoprotein, and both have the capacity of being reproduced exactly alike when they enter a favourable environment. In each cell division the genes are duplicated exactly, although the mechanism by which they can direct the cell to perform this highly complex synthesis is not understood. If an ionizing particle (electron, proton, or α-particle) on traversing the cell loses sufficient energy (i.e. produces an ionization) within or very close to a gene, this will be chemically changed (i.e. a mutation has occurred). The changed gene can be inactivated so that it cannot fulfil its biological function and the factor for which it is responsible will no longer be produced during the development of the embryo. This mutation by loss will be perpetuated, since the germ cells of the offspring carry an identical copy of the genes in the fertilized egg and in each division the gene will be made in its damaged form. Alternatively, the chemical change may have been more subtle and the gene affected by the radiation will not have become inactivated, but will function differently. This gives rise to a modification which will continue until, by a remote chance, another mutation occurs in the same gene.

THE KIND OF MUTATION PRODUCED

The most obvious genetic changes are those which can be seen, such as changes in the colour of eyes, hair, or pigmentation. Even more striking are gross anatomical changes, and a number of these in the case of the fruit-fly are illustrated in Plate 13. These monsters differ from those produced by irradiation of the embryo in that they recur exactly in all subsequent generations. Different colonies of flies with the abnormalities shown in Plate 13 are in existence, and they have all been carried through many generations. The flies whose photographs are shown are at least three generations removed from the parent fly which had been irradiated.

Although a very large number of visible mutations have been produced experimentally in fruit-flies and a few in very large-scale experiments with mice, these are relatively infrequent. Much more common are mutations involving some of the myriad of physiological processes required to keep an animal alive. These detrimental mutations are revealed in animal experiments as a reduction in life-span, general fitness, or vitality. These mutations are the kind which are of the greatest danger to human population, since they give us the hereditary defectives who in extreme cases go to asylums and hospitals, and in less severe cases lead the frustrated life of the partially unfit.

A frequent mutation, and one which can be measured rather simply, is the so-called dominant lethal. Here a mutation has occurred which makes it impossible for the individual to survive. The function controlled by the mutated gene is so vital that if it is lost or altered the organism cannot live. In mammals different types of lethal mutations have been distinguished by the period at which they cause the embryo to die or become reabsorbed. Thus after irradiation of the germinal cells litter sizes are reduced, and this partial sterility is due not to the killing of sperm or ova, since these can be seen to be fully viable, but to the production of a lethal mutation in some of the cells of the reproductive organs which then give rise to defective germ cells. These mutations are not harmful to the population, since they cannot be perpetuated, unless they become so frequent as to introduce a serious decrease in fertility. Their very character ensures their immediate elimination. The mutated gene has to be dominant if it is to be revealed immediately. At least an equal number of the mutations will be recessive and remain hidden until by chance – perhaps many generations after the irradiation – two animals both of which carry this recessive gene are mated. Then a proportion of the offspring will receive the recessive gene from both father and mother, when it will receive expression in the phenotype.

CUMULATIVE AND IRREVERSIBLE

Because the gene determines its own reproduction genetic damage is quite irreversible. Repair and restitution cannot occur, as they do in radiation sickness. Once the mutation has occurred it will be passed on to its descendants until it is eliminated by natural selection. Gene mutations are therefore largely, if not entirely, independent of dose rate, and the number produced by a certain dose will be the same whether this be received during a millionth part of a second, as in an atomic explosion, or over the whole of the sexually active life cycle; irradiation of old animals which can no longer reproduce is no longer genetically hazardous. The contrast between this situation and the extreme dose dependence of the other biological effects of radiation cannot be overstressed. Where repair is possible no serious damage will result if the radiation is given at low dose rate. For example, 300 r received in less than a day is extremely serious to man and survival is not certain. Yet if this same dose is received over thirty years at the rate of 0·2 r/week it is below the tolerance level for workers, such as hospital staff, who handle radioactive materials and machines. But from a genetic point of view the damage is identical, since the same number of mutations will have been produced. In fact radiation at high intensity may be less harmful genetically, since by completely destroying some of the germ cells it prevents mutations from appearing. At low intensities the function of the cells as a whole is not impaired, and every mutation in the reproductive organs will give rise to germ cells carrying the mutation.

The germ plasma keeps a full account of the total amount of ionizing radiation received, whether given off by the dials of luminous watches, from radioactive fall-out of atomic explosions, or during medical treatment or examination. For the symptoms of radiation sickness there is a lower limit of dose below which they are not observed at all. This is not the case with mutations, where every irradiation contributes to the total score, and genetically any exposure to radiation, whatever the dose, is harmful.

Measures which reduce general cellular effects and radiation sickness, such as administration of protective substances, immediately before irradiation (see p. 158) or reducing the amount of oxygen during irradiation (see p. 166) have also decreased in a few cases the number of mutations produced. However, no treatment has yet been found which, applied sometime after irradiation, can reduce the number of mutations; since no recovery is possible from a mutation, no post-irradiation treatment would be expected to restore a mutation. Researches at present being carried out by Dr Alexander Hollaender in the U.S.A. indicate that some mutations can be prevented from occurring if certain chemicals are supplied immediately after irradiation. So far successful results have been obtained only with bacteria, but these experiments suggest that genetic damage may not be quite as final and inevitable as is generally believed. The concept that once a gene has been mutated only natural selection can eliminate it can be retained, but it is possible that the mutation does not follow immediately on the uptake of energy by the cell. For other effects of radiation there is good evidence (see p. 67) that the actual damage is done by the metabolism of the cell itself, and radiation merely initiates the process. If this were also the case for mutations, then, by intervening immediately after irradiation, the number of genes affected might be reduced.

The harmful effects of genetic damage concern the population as a whole and not the individual, since mutations are rare and the chance of a particular parent having an abnormal child as a result of a mutation is small, even after exposure to doses which exceed the tolerance level. But because all mutations are cumulative and persist, the mutagenic action of radiation is a social problem involving the total number of new mutations in a population. One or two people receiving a heavy dose, or even a relatively small group exposed to tolerance doses, is unimportant from this point of view. What matters is the total dose received by the whole population, and this is made up of the radiation received by the large majority who do not come into contact with radiations during their work.

'BACKGROUND' RADIATION

Everything on this earth and, for that matter, anywhere in the universe is exposed to some atomic radiation. This is called the 'background', which is made up of cosmic radiations and the rays given off from the radioactive isotopes present in the body and the normal environment. For convenience the dose received will be expressed in milliroentgen (mr = 1/1,000th part of a roentgen) per year. Cosmic radiations come to us from outer space and are probably emitted by stars. The intensity of cosmic radiations falls off as they enter the earth's atmosphere, being greatest at high altitudes and decreasing as sea level is reached (see Table VII). Man receives an appreciable dose

TABLE VII

Altitude	*Radiation dose from cosmic rays alone (mr/year)*	*Total radiation dose received from normal background including cosmic rays and natural radioactivity (mr/year)*		
		Open ocean	*Ordinary granite*	*Typical sedimentary rock*
Sea level	33	53	143	76
5,000 feet	40	—	150	83
10,000 feet	80	—	190	123
15,000 feet	160	—	270	203
20,000 feet	300	—	414	347

The values also depend slightly on the latitude and the values given apply to the Equator.

from the natural radioactivity of the body itself. This is made up of the radiations given off by the very small amounts of radium which we ingest in one of many ways and which concentrate in the bones (see p. 150) as well as by radiations from the naturally occurring radioactive isotopes which constitute a minute fraction of all the carbon and potassium of the body. The total dose received in this way is of the order of 30 mr per year.

The most important (at least for those of us living at about sea level) contribution to background comes from the radiations given off by the small quantities of radioactive materials present in the surrounding rock and soil. Sedimentary rock gives off much less than granite, which has a higher content of the radioactive elements uranium and thorium. Average values for the background from external radiation is shown in Table VII. A notable feature is the great variation; a sailor who never comes to port receives only one-fifth of the dose of the inhabitant of the high plateau in Tibet. Even within one locality there are great differences, as is shown by measurements made in Sweden (Table VIII). The dose inside a concrete house is

TABLE VIII

Experimental measurements of background in different situations

Streets of Stockholm	121–150	mr/year
Wooden house	104	„
Brick and concrete house	145–300	„
Streets of Brookhaven (town in New York State)	98	„
Streets of Leeds	94	„

higher than that in a wooden one, because slightly radioactive structures completely surround the rooms. The dose received from natural radioactivity and from cosmic rays lies therefore somewhere between 150 and 400 mr per year, and there is nothing very much we can do about it; we cannot escape the 30 mr/year from our own bodies; if we protect ourselves against cosmic rays by going deep below ground we receive instead a much larger dose from minerals, unless we can dig a deep cave in chalk. The background in the tunnels of the London Underground is higher than that on an 11,000 ft. high observatory in Switzerland!

In addition to the normal background civilized man is exposed to radiation from a number of sources. These include some apparently trivial ones, such as the radium in the luminous paint on the dial of a watch. This can amount to as much as 40 mr/year to the sex organs and can therefore add quite appreciably to the total dose received.* Much

* An aeroplane pilot often sits in front of 100 instruments, each with an intensely luminescent dial; there he receives about 0·15 mr per hour, or in a hundred hours of flying a dose equivalent to the normal 'back-

more serious, however, is the radiation received by the reproductive organs during radiological examination. Almost everyone in this country will during his life have had one or more X-ray photographs taken for diagnostic purposes. Chest X-rays are becoming a routine for many every few years, and the mass X-ray service is continually extending. Surgeons and physicians rely more and more on X-rays for diagnosis, and there can be no doubt that advances in this technique have contributed substantially to the progress of medicine. The doses received, except perhaps in some very special cases (see p. 110) will not do any harm to the individual. From a genetic aspect the increasing use of X-ray examination presents a danger because almost the whole population is involved. The dose received by the reproductive organs varies very much with the site examined. In an X-ray of the skull only 0·2 mr is received, while examination of the pelvis results in a dose of about 1 r (i.e. 1,000 mr) which is more than the normal 'background' for five years. There can, of course, be no question of discontinuing or severely restricting X-ray examinations because of a possible genetic risk, but physicians and surgeons should remember that radiography presents the greatest exposure to atomic radiations which the ordinary person is likely to experience – even in the atomic age – and for this reason they should keep their requirements to the absolute minimum. The dose received – often by children from X-ray machines in shoe shops – can be quite high, and a good case can be made out for persuading the shops to discontinue their use, since the information obtained is at best trivial and possibly quite worthless. Less dangerous aids to salesmanship can surely be devised.

ground' for a year. A pilot is probably exposed to a higher dose of radiation than the large majority of people who work in atomic factories or research establishments; certainly much more than the employees of atomic power stations will receive. The only section of the population of this country who regularly receive doses of this order – and for a 40-hour working week this is 6 mr or about a twentieth of the accepted tolerance dose of 0·14 r/week (i.e. 140 mr/week) – are certain hospital personnel. Where uranium is mined the position is different (see p. 148).

The class of people at greatest risk are the uranium miners, whose high incidence of lung cancer is considered in the next chapter. The 'background' in a mine from which ore containing 0·1 per cent uranium (the lowest grade which is commercially useful) is obtained, will be of the order of 5,000 mr per year; in most uranium mines the ore is richer and the background will be correspondingly greater. The actual dose received by the miners is much higher, because they ingest dust which contains radioactive substances. Genetically the numbers involved are too small to contribute significantly to the genetic load of the world's population, and in considering safety measures probably only the cancer risks have to be considered.

5R PER GENERATION

We can now return to the question – What is the maximum dose of radiation, additional to that from the normal background, which can be given to large sections of the population without causing serious harm? A lower limit can be set at about 100 mr/year, since variation in normal background is of this order. In areas with outcrops of granite, such as large parts of Sweden and Scotland, the background may be as much as 100 mr/year greater than in London. Yet peoples who have lived in the high background areas for thousands of years have not shown more genetic abnormalities than those in other civilized countries. This argument cannot be necessarily extended to the highlands of Tibet and Peru, where the background may be 400 r greater than that in England without apparently producing genetic disturbances. These communities are much more primitive and selection pressure may therefore be more effective in eliminating defectives. These general considerations indicate that an extra dose of some 5 r (50 years of 100 mr/year) per generation is unlikely to be genetically serious, and we can certainly afford to tolerate an increase in irradiation of this magnitude. Although we must stress that not even the most pessimistic estimate for the increase in 'background' as a result of the large-scale development of nuclear power is of this magnitude.

There has been considerable discussion about the danger of the increase in 'background' due to the worldwide dissemination of radioactive dust following test explosions of hydrogen bombs. Part of the radioactive material settles out fairly quickly within a few hundred miles' radius of the explosion and produces dose levels which give radiation sickness (see p. 89). The remainder – the proportion depends on the method of explosion – is carried round the world and slowly settles out. According to Sir John Cockcroft the dose received at ground level from all the hydrogen bombs exploded at the time of his statement (20 April 1955) is 0·1 r. Since all the radioactive material has not yet settled out, we continue to receive radiation due to these bombs, and the total accumulated dose is likely to be 0·3 r. Since this statement more hydrogen bomb tests have been carried out, so that the total dose in store for us from these bombs may be as much as 1 r. It must be stressed that this is the dose received in the open, and inside a house it will be less than one-tenth of this value, so there is no foundation for alarmist views expressed about the dangers from test explosions so far, since the dose received per generation is less than one-tenth of that which would be harmful in the most conservative estimate based on the general experience of civilized life on this globe. The position would be different if the testing of hydrogen weapons continued indefinitely, and there is every reason for calling a halt to it. In addition to the genetic risk there is a cancer risk from radioactive fall-out; this is considered in the next chapter.

DOUBLING THE MUTATION RATE

Only experimental work can provide a definite value for the dose which would be dangerous if received by whole populations. To get this figure three pieces of information are necessary: (1) How much can the mutation rate be increased over the normal spontaneous rate* without endangering a civilized population? (2) What is the spontaneous mutation rate in man? (3) By how much does 1 r increase the mutation rate? Experiment cannot answer the first question directly, and we have to rely on the opinions of geneticists; these differ, of course, but surprisingly the disagreement is not so wide as might have been expected. Some, including J. H. Muller, consider that to double the natural mutation rate generation after generation would lead to disaster in a civilized community, and he advocates protective measures to limit the dose to one quarter of that required to produce the doubling. The most conservative estimate is that a doubling of the rate would be detectably deleterious, but not disastrous. So that the divergence in opinion only introduces a factor of two which, bearing all the uncertainties in mind, is quite satisfactory.

The answer to our other two questions is accurately known for fruit-flies, and valuable information is becoming available for mice from the Oak Ridge laboratories in the U.S.A. What can only be called a mouse factory has been established there to make it possible to breed and study sufficient animals – the numbers run into many hundreds of thousands – to get reliable genetic data. The individual genes in mice are about ten times as sensitive as those of fruit-flies, but the total number of spontaneous mutations is higher, so that the dose necessary to double the number of mutations is about the same for mice as for fruit-flies – about 50 r. The extension from mouse to man is extremely difficult and there are factors working in opposite directions. For example, the individual genes in man are probably still more sensitive than those in mice, but on the other hand there are many more of them. Estimates for doubling have varied from about 3 to 150 r per generation. The lower

* The cause of the so-called spontaneous mutations is not known. The radiation background can only be responsible for a very small fraction of the total number of mutations, which occur all the time. Most spontaneous mutations are probably caused by ordinary physiological processes within the germ cells, but it is possible that they are brought about by external factors of which we have as yet no knowledge.

value conflicts with the dose which we know to be safe, and most workers in the field think that the value chosen by Muller, 80 r per generation, is the most reasonable value for the doubling of mutations. If his conclusion is accepted, then the danger limit must lie between 20 and 80 r, received during the period of sexual maturity. The London 'background' is 0·1 r/year, or say 4 r per generation, and the danger limit lies somewhere between 5 and 50 times the ordinary background. To be sure, this gives us a safety factor to play with, but the margin is none too great, especially when the increase in radiological examination is taken into account. The tolerance dose of individual workers of 0·3 r/week (about 600 r per generation) is considerably above the most conservative figure for genetic danger, and there can be no question of using this as a safe limit for irradiations of large numbers of people. Clearly, much more work is needed to define these doses more closely and one must agree with the words of Professor C. H. Waddington: 'Even if we cannot discover a cure for the ills that we may be inflicting on future generations we ought at least to take trouble to find out so that we can decide how far we shall go in running up biological debts which our descendants will have to pay.'

The apparent normality of children born to survivors of the Hiroshima and Nagasaki atom bomb attacks, who had received several hundred roentgen, does not invalidate the dose levels for genetic damage which have just been deduced. One of the reasons is that very few mutations are dominant enough to be immediately recognized when inherited from only one parent. They do, however, add to the genetic load, and payment will be exacted at some stage in a future generation. The other reason is the difficulty of analysing non-uniform groups of any animals, such as are found outside the laboratory. Even with a pure strain of fruit-fly it is not possible to demonstrate mutagenic action by mere inspection of the individuals of the first generation, and only exact genetic methods, which cannot be applied to man, will reveal these. In the case of the Japanese bomb victims the genetic damage will be spread rapidly over large sections of the population as a result of intermarriage with partners who have not been exposed, and no conspicuous permanent damage will be found which can be ascribed to the bombings. The mutations produced will merely increase, by a small amount, the genetic load carried by the Japanese as a whole. To quote Muller, 'The genetically damaged population will eventually have to pay the cost, but this will be spread out over so many small instalments and so intermingled with the greater weight of other payments as hardly to be recognizable.'

PRACTICAL APPLICATION

Under controlled conditions, increasing the mutation rate by irradiation can be of considerable value to plant breeders, and others who otherwise have to wait for chance mutations to give them an improved type. Here the scientist selects the one favourable mutation, out of thousands of harmful ones which are thrown away. Muller envisaged this useful application in the last sentence of his publication in 1928 in which he announced the discovery that radiation produced mutations.

In a typical experiment thousands of barley seeds are irradiated with very high doses from which only a small fraction survive. The seeds are then planted out and on inspecting the crop a number of plants will be seen to be different from the others (see Plates 12a and b). If this difference persists in the next generation of plants, a new mutant will have been established. In Sweden many thousands of such mutants were produced, but only one or two of them were found to have improved properties which made them useful in practice. For example, one type tested regularly in large field trials for many years gave on average 1·7 per cent more grain and 16 per cent more straw, giving a production superiority of 9 per cent; but it required four days longer to attain maturity than the type from which it was derived. Another mutant gives markedly (+15 per cent) better results if grown in eastern Sweden, where it is dry, while it is inferior to the mother strain in very wet years.

Other successes have been the development of strains resistant to certain diseases, such as oats resistant to rust and peanuts to leaf-spot. New and attractive varieties of flowers have also been produced in this way. The most useful application has been in the field of antibiotics. The amount of penicillin produced by the mould has been increased many times by producing a favourable mutation. Millions of spores were irradiated, and those showing improved penicillin yield were selected. Without the development of these new mutations penicillin would not now be freely available all over the world. The use of radiations to accelerate the production of mutations is only beginning, and in time the benefits may even be extended to animal breeding. But even if it is confined to botany we can expect very many useful advances. A point which must be remembered when contrasting these developments with the genetic hazards is that in these experiments one particular property is selected which has an overall advantage under a narrow range of conditions. The new strain may well be inferior to the mother strain in other respects, and only show a positive advantage in the artificial environment for which it is intended.

CHAPTER 5

THE TWO-EDGED SWORD–CANCER CURE AND CAUSE

IT is a tragic paradox that atomic radiations both cure and cause cancer. The first unambiguous evidence for a malignant tumour caused by radiation was found only three years after these selfsame rays had produced a complete cure of a skin cancer in a woman. The reason for this apparent contradiction lies in the complex action of atomic radiations on the cell. The use of atomic radiations for the cure and control of tumours depends on their immediate lethal action, whereas the production of cancers is a long-delayed effect, not directly related to cell death but probably the result of a subtle cell modification.

Cancer cannot be defined by one characteristic. The principal features which taken together constitute a malignant growth are, firstly, multiplication of cells at a particular point in excess of those required by the body. Cell proliferation occurs normally at a number of sites; the most common of these being outer layers such as skin or the linings of the stomach and the intestine which have to be continually replaced because of wear and tear. Also in the blood-forming organs there is continuous division to provide new cells. Cells not normally dividing can be stimulated by injury or hormonal excretions to multiply; this growth is not malignant, but quite normal, and cell multiplication is therefore not sufficient to define cancer. The ability to invade neighbouring tissue by a process of infiltration between cell colonies is an essential property of a cancer, and one which distinguishes it not only from normal cell multiplication but also from warts, cysts, and other so-called benign growths. From a medical point of view the most dangerous characteristic is the ability of cancer cells which have broken off from the primary centre to settle at a new site and there to form a secondary growth which may be even more harmful than the original tumour. Cancer cells can be transported in the blood stream, the lymph channels, or across body cavities to distant parts. At the new site a tumour will grow which has the characteristics of the primary growth, and this may make it possible to determine the site of origin of a secondary growth; indeed the existence of an unrecognized primary growth may be revealed in this way. At the primary site the malignant growth has some of the properties of the tissue from which it arose. A fraction of these tumour cells differentiate to turn into cells with a defined physiological function such as the production of hormonal secretions. This same behaviour persists in the secondary deposits, and a patient with an advanced tumour of the thyroid will have growths showing thyroid behaviour in a number of different parts of the body.

From a clinical point of view cancer is not a single disease, but a term which comprises a whole group of conditions each with its own characteristic symptoms and differing widely in seriousness. Some cancers can be cured in almost every case, others can be treated successfully only if detected early, and there is the steadily diminishing group where the chance of a complete cure is small and where the role of medicine is confined to alleviating the symptoms. An important class of malignant diseases which are not normally classified as cancer are disorders of the blood-forming organs which result in an overproduction of white blood cells (leukaemia) or red blood cells (polycythaemia). Although from a purely technical point of view these are not cancers, leukaemia is a malignant condition which results from a change in the cells of the blood-forming organs which is of exactly the same type as that which elsewhere in the body gives rise to 'solid' tumours, and the cause and cure of leukaemia involve the same considerations.

The key to malignancy lies in the behaviour of the cancer cell. It is not the faculty for unlimited growth that distinguishes this from the normal cell. The capacity to multiply is the property of all cells which have not become too highly differentiated; the growth which occurs when a cut is repaired is much faster than that of most cancers, but it stops when the wound has closed. The normal cell is under the control of the body while the malignant cell is not. The important conclusion is that during the transformation from normal to malignant the cell does not gain a new function but loses the mechanism which brings it under the control of the whole organism. To consider cancer as a deficiency explains why it is relatively easy to make a normal cell malignant, but up to now the reverse process has not been brought about. All the methods of treating a cancer aim therefore at the eradication of the cancer cells either by killing them or by making them incapable of further division. The role of the surgeon is obvious, but there are many deep-seated tumours which are inaccessible or involve organs where an operation would be too dangerous, and for these the treatment is exposure to atomic radiations. In the last few years certain chemical substances (see Chapter 11) have been added to the armoury of the physician as adjuncts to radiation therapy, and for certain types of leukaemia these chemicals offer the best treatment possible.

Because progress has been gradual and there has been no spectacular new treatment the advances which have been made in the control of cancer are not obvious and are often not appreciated. There has nevertheless been a steady improvement which is not immediately obvious from the statistics published by the Registrar-General. The incidence of cancer increases sharply with increase in age (see Fig. 26) and for a true comparison it is therefore necessary to compare groups of people of the same age, since the average age of the population has been increasing continuously for many years. If there had been no change in the true (or age-specific) death-rate for cancer, then the deaths from cancer per thousand as given in the usual statistics should show a steady increase over the last quarter of a century as the average age of the population increased. The only way of obtaining a true assessment of the way in which cancer is being tackled by medicine is by comparing in different years the percentage of the population which dies of cancer at a particular age. When this is done it can be seen that mortality from cancer at most sites (see Figs. 27 and 28) has decreased steadily over the last twenty-five years. There is only one important exception, namely lung cancer. Here the increase in the case of males has been so great as to out-

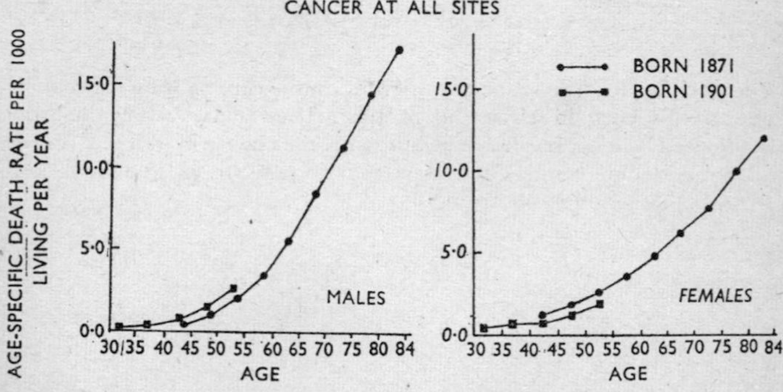

Fig. 26 – Increase in the death rate from cancer of all kinds with increasing age. The figures apply to the groups of people born in 1871 and in 1901. The first group are now more than eighty years old; while those of the second group are now in their fifties.

weigh the decrease from death from other types of cancer, and as a result deaths from all cancers put together show a true increase (see Fig. 26). In women the number dying from lung cancer is much less than in men, and as a result the cancer rate has not gone up. There is every reason to suspect that lung cancer is induced by an external factor (smoking?) which has increased in intensity in the last twenty years, and it should therefore be omitted from figures used to determine the change in the effectiveness of treatment of cancer over the years. When lung cancer is excluded the figures show a steady decrease in the death-rate from cancer, even for men. How much of this decrease

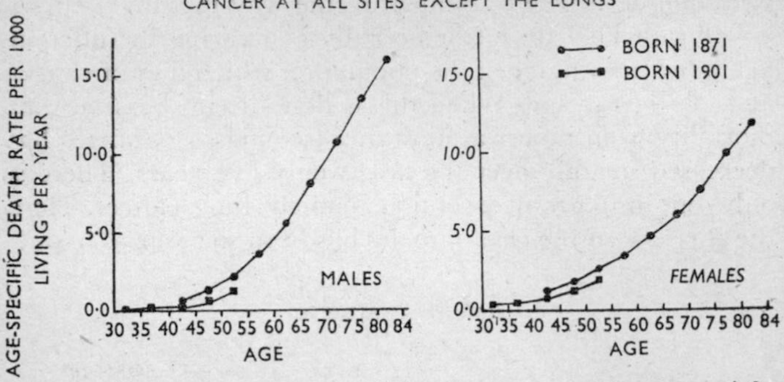

Fig. 27 – Deaths from cancer at all sites (but excepting lung cancer) for age groups born in 1871 and in 1901. These curves show that the incidence of cancer has fallen steadily, i.e. the chance of dying of cancer (other than lung cancer) at fifty years is 50 per cent less for those born in 1901 than for those born in 1871.

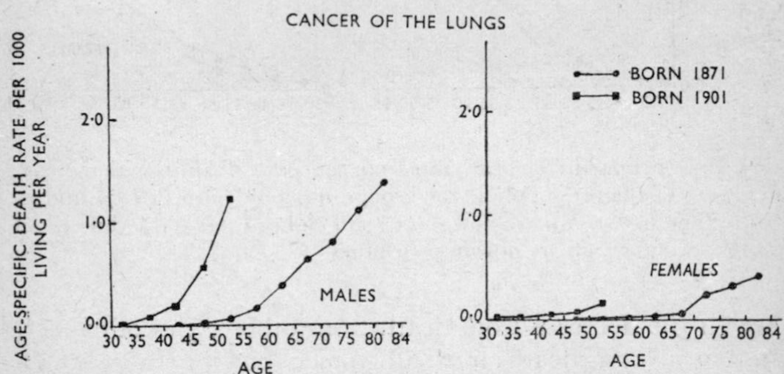

Fig. 28 – Deaths from cancer of the lungs. The incidence is much greater for men than for women, but with both there is no doubt that in the more recent generations many more die from this disease than in the older generations. Thus the chance of a man dying of lung cancer who reached fifty within the last ten years is about twenty times as great as that of a man who reached fifty in 1921–31.

is due to a reduction in incidence and how much to improvements in treatment of the disease once it has arisen is a matter of speculation, but it shows that modern medicine is successfully tackling this disease. But for lung cancer, which should be considered a social problem, rather like road accidents, progress in the treatment and control of malignant diseases might give cause for congratulation rather than the alarm at present felt. To the improvements in treatment many factors contribute; probably the most important is earlier diagnosis and more accurate location of tumours. New techniques, drugs, and anaesthetics have increased the successes of cancer surgery in general, and in certain special cases spectacular results have been obtained.

RADIATION THERAPY

The aim of all treatments is the complete removal of all malignant cells while producing a minimum of damage to the surrounding tissue. Where the radiation can be confined entirely to the tumour the problem is relatively simple; a dose must be given which will kill all the cells. There is, however, a limit to the rate at which such a dose can be given, since debris of the dead cell must be removed and assimilated by the surrounding tissue. If the cancer mass destroyed at any one time is too great the system as a whole will be poisoned and severe sickness can follow the irradiation. For this as well as other reasons the treatment must be spread out, and the patient is usually given a number of treatments.

In general the real problem is to treat the tumour without destroying the tissue in which it grows or damaging the skin and tissue which lie between the tumour and the X-ray machine. It is here that variations in behaviour between different cancers are most marked; for some the best results are obtained with frequent irradiations, giving a relatively small dose each time, while other tumours become resistant to radiation under these conditions and may be rendered untreatable by irradiation. For these it is necessary to apply the X-rays in the shortest time which the patient can tolerate.

Where the difference between the radiosensitivity of the tumour and of the surrounding tissue is great, the radiotherapist has the best chance of success, and sensitive tumours may be destroyed by a total dose of 2,500 r, given perhaps in six instalments. With other tumours the margin between killing the tumour and destroying its bed is small, and then treatment is difficult, since successful eradication of the malignant growth may make it necessary to cause extensive damage to healthy tissue. Yet if some cancer cells survive, the tumour will reappear, and may not respond to irradiation again. A tumour cell which has escaped in this way may lie dormant for years; its growth will be held up because of the cellular damage it has sustained, and because the surrounding tissue is not healthy and does not provide a satisfactory environment for parasitic growth. Although the tumour cell is an independent unit and is beyond the control of the organ or tissue of which it once formed a part, it still requires nutriment and oxygen for growth. For these it relies on the healthy tissue of the tumour bed, and if this is destroyed its growth is bound to be retarded. Destruction of the tumour bed without killing the tumour will arrest the progress of the disease temporarily until the cancer cells have found new host tissue.

After irradiation a tumour may shrink rapidly, but a cure has not necessarily been obtained, since a few cells may have survived. On the other hand the size of the tumour mass may not be decreased after irradiation and the lump which is felt may be as big as before; yet a complete cure can have been achieved. In this case irradiation has not killed the tumour cells, but has caused them to differentiate (see p. 42) further so that they have become incapable of further division. The tumour has been 'sterilized', but may not disappear for some time, since the differentiated cells can have a long life. These examples illustrate the difficulties of predicting the course and outcome of a radiation treatment. In spite of much research it is not possible to predict with certainty the response of a particular tumour to irradiation, and there are no tests by which the radiation resistance can be determined beforehand; or, more important, whether a tumour is likely to become more resistant as irradiation proceeds.

The way in which tumour cells are killed or sterilized is not fully understood. Experiments described in Chapter 2 showed that rapidly dividing cells were more sensitive than those of adult tissue which divide infrequently or which were fully differentiated and thus no longer capable of division. The sensitive dividing cells do not die immediately after irradiation, but only when they attempt division in a subsequent mitosis. At first sight this behaviour would appear to explain why it is possible to destroy tumour cells which are multiplying without at the same time killing the 'stationary' tumour bed. More detailed studies have shown that radiosensitivity is not invariably related to growth rate and that in most treatments destruction of the tumour occurs before every one of the constituent cancer cells has entered division. If the cells were only killed as a result of chromosome breaks which mechanically interfere with later mitosis, treatments would have to be very protracted to ensure that all cells were affected, since the cells are only sensitive to radiation shortly before division. The mechanism by which radiation eradicates tumours is complex and includes, in addition to effects on the cancer cells themselves, injury to the tumour bed and general physiological changes in the patient brought about by radiation.

METHODS OF TREATMENT

For tumours near the surface X-rays produced by conventional equipment, such as 250 kV generators, are usually used. The plan of treatment depends on the type of cancer, and every effort is made to restrict the irradiation to the affected parts only. An important factor is the dose received by the skin, since this is relatively sensitive to radiation (see p. 102) and is severely damaged by the doses ranging in most cases from 2,000 to 7,000 r which are necessary to kill or sterilize the tumour. Skin reaction is prevented in most cases by irradiating the tumour from a number of directions (see Fig. 29). To plan such a treatment it is essential to know the position of the tumour as accurately as possible;

the different beams are arranged to cross within a small volume of tissue which in this way receives the maximum dose. The therapy equipment has to be highly movable so that a patient can be irradiated from any angle.

If for effective treatment it is necessary to irradiate large volumes of the body, particularly in the abdomen, the tolerance dose may not be determined by the skin but by radiation sickness of the kind which follows whole body

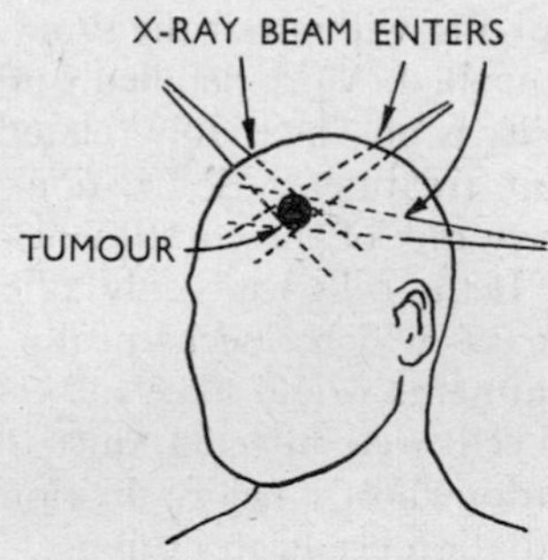

Fig. 29 – Method of treating a tumour with X-rays so as to reduce skin reaction. The X-rays are made to enter the head from a number of different directions, and converge on the tumour.

exposure. This problem arises when the tumours are deep-seated; and new very high voltage equipment, in general only available since the end of the war, is helping to overcome this problem. X-rays become attenuated as they enter the body and the intensity falls the deeper they go. Fig. 7 shows that using 400 kV X-rays tissue four inches inside the body receives only one-third of the dose given to the skin. The penetration of X-rays increases with their energy, and the decrease in intensity of two-million-volt (2MV) X-rays is already much less. With even higher energies the position becomes still more favourable, since a number of physical factors conspire together to produce an intensity maximum within the irradiated tissue; for example, with 24 MV

X-rays the radiation is at its most intense two inches below the skin and the surface dose is less than that deep within the body. With machines of this type it is possible to focus the radiation on to an internal tumour and thereby reduce both skin and general 'whole body' type of reaction. A number of different types of machines are available for producing these million-volt X-rays, and two of these are illustrated in Plates 14 and 15. In addition to the problem of producing the high voltage the machines must be highly manoeuvrable, so that the patient can be irradiated from all directions. Each one of these installations is a major engineering project, for all operations have to be remote-controlled because the great penetrating power of the radiations makes it necessary for all therapy personnel to be outside the treatment room and separated from it by several feet of concrete. In spite of these difficulties a number of these super-voltage machines are operating in Britain and doing valuable work in the treatment of deep-seated tumours.

Radium gives off 2 MeV γ-rays (these are the same as X-rays), and it can therefore be used instead of these high-voltage machines as a source for high-energy radiation. The intensity necessary to keep the time required for individual treatments within reasonable limits makes it necessary to use many grams of radium. Until recently this meant that suitable deep-ray therapy units, where the radiations from radium are used at a distance, were very expensive and radium was usually used in much smaller quantities in the tips of needles which were introduced directly into body tissues.

With the development of atomic energy, man-made isotopes have become available in large quantities and radium is no longer the only source of high-energy γ-rays. A radioactive isotope widely used is cobalt 60 (^{60}Co) which gives off 1·5 MeV radiations. This material is produced in atomic piles and is available in relatively large quantities. Treatment units often referred to as 'cobalt bombs' (Plate 15) are in use which contain as much as 2,000 curies of cobalt (equivalent to more than four pounds of radium) and these give off large amounts of radiation, so that individual treatments take only a few minutes. The armoury of the radiotherapist, which until recently was largely confined to 250 kV X-rays, has thus been vastly extended, and the improvements in results have probably not as yet been fully felt, since it takes a number of years before a course of treatment can be assessed as successful.

TREATMENT WITH RADIOACTIVE ISOTOPES

Undoubtedly the ideal method of applying ionizing radiations in cancer treatment would be by administration of a chemical substance which is taken up only by cancer cells but not by ordinary cells and which contains some radioactive atoms in its molecule. Many attempts have been made to find such substances, but in no case was the localization limited enough to make it possible to give a sufficient dose to the tumour without damaging other tissue. A number of substances have been found which become concentrated in certain specific tumours, but invariably they are also taken up by an organ such as the liver or thyroid gland which was not affected by the disease.

Although tumour selectivity has not been achieved there are some chemical substances which are taken up with a high degree of specificity by one organ only of the body. This makes it possible to give a tumour originating in this organ a high dose of radiation without damaging other parts of the body. The healthy cells in this organ will also be irradiated as a rule, but they are more resistant than the tumour, the cells of which are less highly differentiated. Where applicable this method is to be preferred to deep-ray therapy, described in the previous section, which depends on physical factors for localization and needs very accurate diagnosis of the position of the tumour if irradiation of tissue unrelated to the cancer is to be avoided. The use of radio iodine (^{131}I) for tumours of the thyroid illustrates well the use of isotopes. Iodine is taken up very selectively by the thyroid gland; the radioactive isotope ^{131}I behaves in exactly the same way as ordinary non-active iodine and following its administration the thyroid may be as much as two hundred times as radioactive as the remaining tissue of the body. What is even more favourable is that metastases (tumour cells which have broken away to start secondary growth in other parts of the body) usually retain some thyroid character and therefore also concentrate iodine. Complete cures have been reported for patients with widely disseminated cancers of this type, a condition which without radio iodine could not have been treated.

Another example is the use of radioactive phosphorus (^{32}P) for the treatment of leukaemia (excess of white blood cells) and especially polycythaemia (excess of red blood cells). Here the degree of localization is much smaller since phosphorus is necessary for all growing cells. Because the blood-forming tissues contain a greater proportion of rapidly dividing cells than other organs of the adult body, radioactive phosphorus becomes localized there to some extent. The remainder of the body will, however, also contain some of the radioactive ^{32}P so that the overall effect is an intense dose to the bone-marrow coupled with an irradiation equivalent to a whole body dose. This procedure has given excellent results for polycythaemia and some improvement in leukaemia; ^{32}P will, of course, also concentrate in tumours since they contain dividing cells, but treatment of these with this isotope has not given very successful results. The difference in response of the cancers compared with the blood malignancies is probably due to the fact that the latter respond to whole body irradiation, which is sometimes used for their treatment, while solid tumours do not. The combination of whole body together with localized irradiation inherent in ^{32}P therapy is therefore particularly favourable for the blood diseases.

Direct injection of finely suspended radioactive particles ('radiocolloids') which are quite insoluble in the tissue fluids provides a useful degree of localization of radiation by purely physical means. This type of therapy is used as a routine in many hospitals for the treatment of cancers which are accessible, but where surgical removal is not possible because of closeness to delicate organs. Success is obtained only if treatment is given before any metastases have occurred, since the radiocolloid cannot search these out.

Radioisotopes of other elements, for example sodium (^{24}Na), have been and are being used, and progress in this field is rapid and continuous. Since the discovery of nuclear fission it is possible to prepare radioactive isotopes of nearly all the elements, and many are available at relatively low cost. They are supplied by the atomic energy authorities of the U.K. and U.S.A., who fly them to laboratories and hospitals all over the world. The first isotopes prepared in atomic piles were used in a few hospitals soon after the end of the war, but wide distribution and virtually unlimited supplies have been available only since about 1950. This is too short a period to assess the improvement they have brought about in the treatment of cancer. Except in a few special cases the use of isotopes has not produced cures which could not have been obtained with the best of the other methods of treatment, but their great contribution so far is their relative cheapness, and simplicity in use, which have made treatment available to patients who have no access to the few centres with the most advanced deep X-ray equipment. The daily dispatch of isotopes to the four corners of the globe bears impressive testimony to this.

Although the large-scale production of artificial radioactive isotopes has only been possible since the end of the war, small quantities were prepared in some of the atom-smashing machines built before the war. The first of these, the cyclotron at Berkeley, California, was used for part of its time as early as 1936 for the production of radioisotopes for medical use, and the value of ^{32}P in the treatment of blood cancers was discovered there. As a result twenty years' experience is available to assess the value of this isotope in treatment. The figures justify the claim that polycythaemia can be satisfactorily controlled, and the survival of patients treated with ^{32}P is about equal to that of diabetics treated with insulin. The average survival time of the patients treated was fourteen years, compared with a survival of twenty years for a group of the general population having the same distribution of ages (see Fig. 30). With leukaemia the results obtained with ^{32}P are less satisfactory,

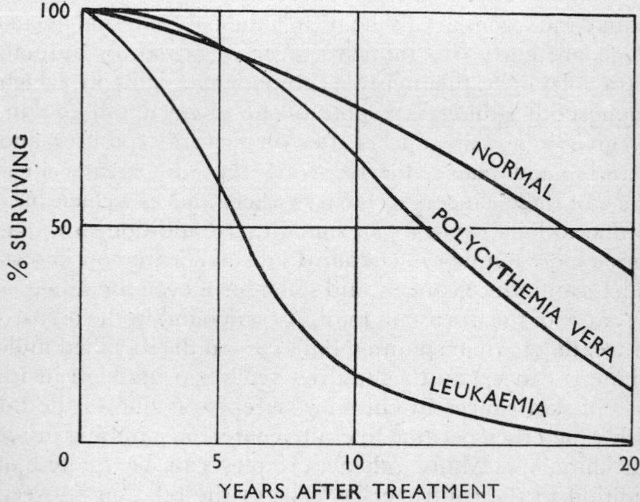

Fig. 30 – Average survival times of patients with the blood diseases polycythaemia and leukaemia after treatment with the radioactive isotope ^{32}P. The survival time for people who had not contracted the disease was computed for a group having the same age distribution as the patients suffering from the malignant blood diseases.

the average survival time from onset of the disease being five years. But even this figure is considerably better than that obtained with other methods of treatment.* There can be little doubt that when sufficient time has elapsed to make an assessment of the new methods for the radiation treat-

* These do not include the newer drugs (see Chapter 11) which have proved most valuable but which have not been in use long enough to obtain long-term survival rates.

ment of tumours, which have been developed within the last ten years, it will be found that they are distinct improvements.

CANCER INDUCTION

Atomic radiations are by no means the only external agents which are known to induce cancer in a man or animal. Ultraviolet light, the invisible component of sunlight, which amongst other things is responsible for giving a 'tan' to skin, can give rise to skin cancers after very severe exposures, and there is good reason for believing that the greater incidence of these cancers in farm workers and fishermen may be due to long exposure to sunlight. In addition to radiations a large number of chemical substances are now known which can induce cancer, and some have been identified as the cause of the disease in man. A compound in the oil used for treating yarn in spinning mills caused the so-called mule spinners' cancer, and a hundred years ago the high incidence of skin cancer in chimney-sweeps was due to the tar with which they became liberally coated on climbing inside the chimneys. Many other examples can be quoted in addition to the controversial issue of the relation between smoking and lung cancer. The proportion of all human cancers which are initiated by an outside stimulus, chemical or radiation, cannot be estimated, but may be substantial. The mechanism by which these agents act is not yet known, but in most cases they are cell poisons which interfere preferentially with rapidly dividing cells. Like atomic radiations most of the chemical carcinogens will arrest growth, and some have been found useful as cancer-controlling drugs (see Chapter 11).

Professor Alexander Haddow, twenty years ago, suggested that the cancer-producing action of all these substances may be the result of prolonged interference with normal growth. In many cases tumours arise only years after the substance has been applied, and even the most potent agents require months before they produce tumours. The hypothesis of Haddow relating growth inhibition to cancer-producing properties led to the recognition of cancer-producing action in many types of cell poisons. The discovery in recent years that a number of those substances as well as atomic radiations and ultra-violet light possess the property of producing mutations (see Chapter 4) led to a revision of the growth inhibition theory, and the view is widely held that it is their mutagenic action which renders them cancer-producing. This aspect will be discussed in more detail at the end of this chapter.

The reference to the cancer-inducing chemicals was made to emphasize that in this respect atomic radiations are in no way unique, but this, of course, does not detract from the importance of their effect. Apart from the genetic factors, production of cancer is probably the most dangerous aspect of exposure to radiation, since malignant conditions can arise from repeated doses at low intensity and from the accumulation of radioactive substances in the bone, without giving any indications of radiation sickness. Reference has already been made to the drama of the doctors who pioneered the medical uses of atomic radiations and whose devotion was repaid by the appearance of debilitating deformities and eventual death from cancer. The emphasis from the scientific point of view is that in most cases cancer appeared twenty years after they had started their work and that it followed only after many exposures which amounted *in toto* to a very high dose. Since the tragic chance discovery of the cancer-producing action of atomic radiations a great deal of work has been done on this problem, and cancer induction can be divided roughly into the following categories:

(1) Very high doses given only to small areas of the body will produce tumours at the site of irradiation usually after long periods.

(2) Non-lethal irradiation given to the whole body can give rise fairly quickly to leukaemia; in man it has been found a few years after irradiation and in mice after a few

months.* If leukaemia has not been produced, then cancer at a number of different sites may appear towards the end of the normal life of the animal.

(3) Instances are known of organs under glandular control (e.g. ovaries) which develop malignant growth after relatively low doses of irradiation, but the data are very limited.

Localized irradiation. There are a number of different examples in man of cancer produced by local irradiation; the skin cancers of the early radiologists have already been mentioned. The largest group in which a high incidence of tumours can be ascribed with reasonable certainty to radiation are the Austrian miners from Schneeberg and Joachimsthal (now called Jáchymow). These mines have been worked for hundreds of years and are rich in radioactive ores. They supplied Madame Curie with her starting material, the mineral pitchblende, from which she isolated radium. The history of the strange disease called 'Bergkrankheit' by the miners goes back to the sixteenth century. In 1879 it was recognized as a cancer which was responsible for three-quarters of all deaths amongst these miners. Another investigator in the early part of this century claimed that this disease was responsible for nearly half the deaths, and more recently figures given in Table IX show that the mortality rate from lung cancer amongst the miners was fifty times that of the normal population. Cancers at other sites were the same in the miners as in the group chosen for comparison. The high incidence is due to the radioactive gas radon which is produced continually as the first decay product of radium (see p. 7). This gas diffuses out of the radium-containing ores into the atmosphere of the mines. Its inhalation is very dangerous since it emits α-particles which have a very high relative biological

* A rough and ready rule for the length of induction period of cancer-producing agents in different species is that the average time before tumours are seen is proportional to the life-span. A month in a mouse corresponds to three or four years in man.

TABLE IX

Cancer mortality for 1,000

	Jáchymow miners	*Schneeberg miners*		*General population of Vienna: (males between 15–79 years for period 1932–6)*
	1929–38	*1895–7*	*1895–1912*	
Lung cancer	9·8	12·7	16·5	0·34
Cancer of other organs	0·7	2·4	2·1	2·1

effectiveness (see p. 206). The average period for the induction of lung cancer was about seventeen years, and during this time the lungs of the miners will have received a dose of at least 1,000 rads and possibly more. From all we know of other cancers this dose is sufficient to induce tumours locally. The working conditions of the miners probably contributed to the very high incidence of 'Berg-krankheit', since they worked several miles away from their village and had twice a day to make long treks with inadequate clothing, often in atrocious weather conditions. This resulted in constant chest disturbance which would favour the retention of radioactive particles and may even predispose to cancer (smokers' cough?).

The unfortunate girls engaged in painting watch and clock dials with luminous paint containing radioactive substances have provided abundant material for assessing the dangers of cancer of the bone from radium and some other radioactive products. When these substances are ingested they may be trapped in the bones and even very small quantities will give rise to a local dose of irradiation sufficient to destroy the bone and induce cancer. Once a substance has got into the bone it almost invariably remains there, and no satisfactory therapeutic measures have been found which prevent the injury from occurring or which remove the radioactive material before it has done irreparable damage. This is why radioactive isotopes of the bone-seeking elements are so exceedingly dangerous. The maximum permissible level of radium permanently incorporated in the skeleton – and the majority of radium taken into the body is fixed in this way – has been laid down by the International Commission on radiological protection as 0·1 microcurie (or approximately 1/250,000th part of an ounce of radium).

It must be stressed that this is the tolerance level for persons whose occupation requires them to be in contact with radium. If for some reason large sections of the population were at risk, the safety limit would have to be set much lower. This is why the committee appointed by the government in 1955 to report on the hazards to man from nuclear explosions were particularly concerned over the danger from the radioactive isotope, strontium 90, which forms a large part of the 'fall-out' (see p. 127) from atomic explosions. This isotope is a bone seeker, and if ingested becomes quickly concentrated in the growing parts of the bone; and this committee believes that the greatest danger from fall-out may be the production of bone cancers and not the genetic damage resulting from irradiation of the gonads. Strontium 90 released in this way gets into water, is deposited on the soil and leaves, and is absorbed and concentrated by plants. Man and animals will therefore consume this isotope with their food and drink, and this will be additional to any which may settle out directly. Grazing animals such as cows are particularly susceptible, and variations of the amount of strontium 90 in milk have been correlated with periods of fall-out from nuclear explosion. So far the amount of radio strontium distributed over the world by fall-out from bombs is completely negligible when compared with our daily intake of radium which is present everywhere since it occurs naturally. Strontium 90 is a β-ray emitter and therefore much less harmful than radium, and the tolerance level is probably ten times that permissible with radium; but the danger of producing bone cancer is a risk as real as that arising from genetic damage if the number of atomic tests continues to increase.

The discovery that radium concentrates in bone and causes cancer was made following the observation that girls who painted dials with paint rendered luminescent by radium and mesothorium (the mesothorium content of the paint is particularly dangerous since it gives off α-rays) became anaemic and developed tumours. It was usual for these workers to 'point' the brushes used by licking them, and in this way they swallowed the radioactive material. When large amounts were swallowed the bone-marrow became affected, and they usually died within a few years from anaemia and haemorrhages and infection. Those who took in smaller quantities developed bone lesions which eventually turned into cancer. The time taken before cancer appeared was, on an average, fifteen years after exposure to the radioactive substance, and this long delay has made it difficult to determine the proportion of these workers who contracted cancer of the bone, since in the interval they have dispersed all over the country, but one suspects that the incidence is very high. Often a patient with this disease has completely forgotten that at some time in the past she worked with radioactive paints. Nowadays the factory inspectors insist on strict safety precautions being followed in this industry, but this industrial hazard had claimed in one small factory in New Jersey alone at least forty-one victims who painted during the ten-year period 1915–26. Only four of the girls who worked there are still alive, and even they contracted non-malignant bone injuries of a severe type.

Another group to swallow harmful amounts of radium were patients suffering from a variety of mental, rheumatic, and other afflictions. It was quite erroneously believed in the 1920s by some physicians that radioactive water could alleviate these conditions, and relatively large quantities were prescribed. More than fifteen years later a number of these patients were found to have bone cancers which could be definitely ascribed to radium, since this substance was subsequently found in their skeletons.

Whole body radiation. There is abundant evidence that all animals which have received high doses of radiation, which has involved the whole body, develop a much larger proportion of tumours in old age than is normally found. The tumours occur a long time after all other symptoms of radiation sickness have disappeared and often occur so late in life that they do not contribute significantly to the shortening of the life-span which follows irradiation (see p. 92). The cancers produced are of many different types and their relative frequency varies very greatly with the strain of the animals used; in some there is a very high incidence of ovarian tumours while in others leukaemia predominates. In a careful experiment with rats (see Fig. 31) as little as 32 r produced a detectable increase in cancer

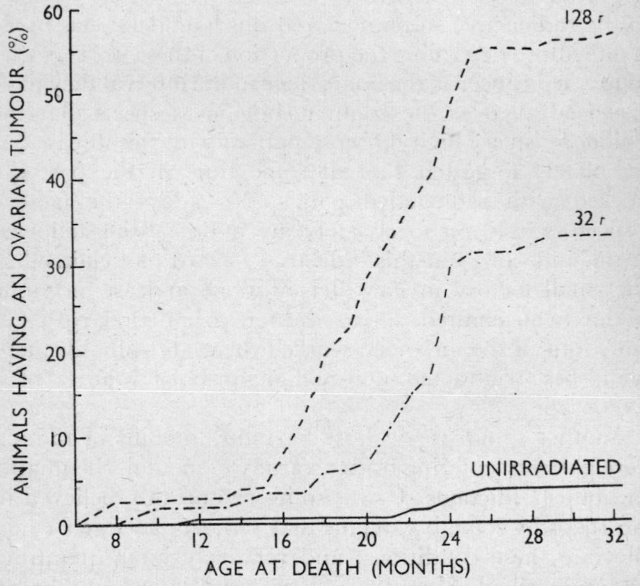

Fig. 31 – Occurrence of ovarian tumours after whole body doses of X-rays of 32 r and 128 r in a particular strain of mice.

of the ovaries. It is, however, the leukaemia incidence which is of the greatest importance, since there is good evidence that this follows severe whole body irradiation in man.

The leukaemia-inducing effect of radiations varies a very great deal from one strain of animal to the next; in some highly inbred mice, which normally have a high incidence of leukaemia, as little as 50 r will produce a significant increase of the disease. In these strains it is possible to produce the disease in almost all the animals by giving fractionated doses (see Fig. 32). In other strains of mice a

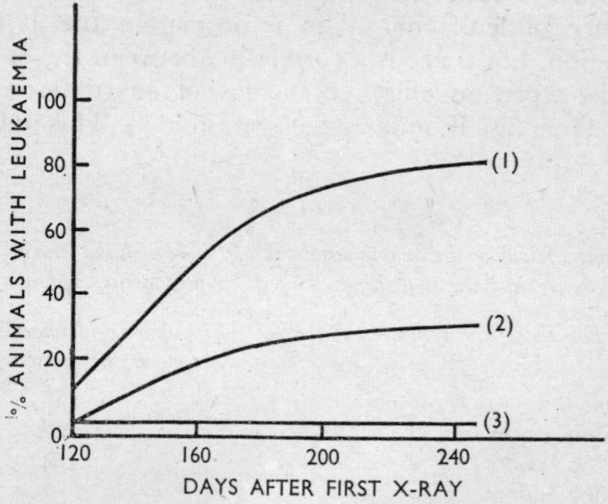

Fig. 32 – Production of leukaemia in young mice following four doses of 160 r separated by one week. (1) Animals irradiated only. (2) Irradiation followed by injection of bone marrow. (3) The thighs of the animals were shielded from irradiation by screening with lead, the remainder of the body was irradiated as before.

significant increase is formed only after a dose of many hundreds of roentgen. Chronic irradiation at a level of not less than 4 r per day also brings about leukaemia. The dose necessary to produce cancers and leukaemia by whole body irradiation varies very much more from one strain to another than the induction of tumours localized by irradiation with big doses. Clearly genetic factors – one might call them inherited predispositions – are very important in determining whether the general upset caused by whole body irradiation will result in cancer or not. For this reason the data from experimental animals cannot help us in determining the dose which is likely to induce leukaemia in man.

Unhappily the atom bombs dropped on Japan have provided the necessary information. Not only has it been shown that the victims who had been exposed to the bomb and had survived the other effects had a much higher incidence of leukaemia than is normal in the Japanese population, but there is a correlation between the distance from the explosion (this gives the dose of radiation received) and the increase in leukaemia (see Table x). This indicates

TABLE X

Incidence of leukaemia among survivors of the Hiroshima atomic bomb exposed at various distances from the centre of the explosion

Distance from centre (metres)	*Incidence of leukaemia (per 10,000 persons)*
Less than 1,000 metres	128
1,000–1,500	28
1,500–2,000	4
2,000–3,000	2
3,000 or more	1·6
Normal Japanese population	about 1·5

that as little as 50 r received in one dose increases slightly, but none the less significantly, the chance of developing leukaemia later.

If the irradiation is protracted or intermittent the harmful limits are not known, but it has been stated that the death-rate from leukaemia among American radiologists is about ten times greater than that of American physicians who do not occupationally come into contact with atomic radiations. The way this information has been collected is not entirely satisfactory, and the exact magnitude of the increase is in question; but there can be no doubt that there is an increase which proves that chronic irradiation at low levels produces this disease in man. This conclusion is borne out by an increase in leukaemia in patients who had received radiation which involved exposing nearly their whole body, as treatment for a disease which affects the joints of the spine. From the Japanese cases the average length of time between irradiation and appearance of leukaemia symptoms is about six years. This is in marked contrast with tumours produced by local irradiation which may have a latent period of twenty years or more; and even the average period of fifteen years for the uranium miners is short compared with the appearance of skin tumours following a high local dose.

HOW ARE CANCER CELLS PRODUCED?

The transition from ordinary to malignant is a change which is transmitted to every daughter cell. In some respects therefore the act of making a normal cell into a cancer one is akin to a mutation. The genes which determine the characteristic of the cell have been altered in some way, and this change is perpetuated and has never been reversed, probably because it involves a loss of function. Such a process has been called a somatic mutation, since it involves differentiated cells and not germ cells as in ordinary mutations (see Chapter 4). Although every cell in the body carries a full set of chromosomes which presumably carry all the genes, only a few of these play any part in a differentiated cell. All the genes are necessary for the development of the fertilized egg into the animal with all its many organs. Once the process of differentiation has taken place to produce cells which have a special function (skin, liver, etc.), then the majority of the genes must become redundant. The cells which carry them can manage very well without them, in rather the same way as human beings can without their appendix. This is why differentiated cells can survive relatively large doses of radiation which bring about observable changes in their chromosomes.

Usually the cell is killed only if the damage to the chromosomes is so severe (e.g. bridge formation) as to impede mechanically the delicate movements in mitosis. According to the somatic mutation theory of cancer production, some of the genes play a part even in the differentiated cells, and a cancer cell is produced if those genes are affected which are responsible for the mechanism which maintains the cell under the influence of the body as a whole. Since atomic radiation produces true mutations, this theory explains the cancer-producing action of these radiations in a simple manner. Cancer results when the right mutation occurs, and this may require very large doses. When, for example, the cells of an area of the skin are bombarded, many cells die, but eventually in one of them the cancer mutation is induced and a malignant growth then starts.

This attractive theory cannot apply in its simplest form, for a number of reasons. Mutations are independent of dose rate, and the chance of obtaining the cancer mutation should therefore be the same whether an area of skin has received 5,000 r in one go or at the rate of 1 r per day for fifteen years. This is not observed; the cancer incidence depends on dose rate. Even more difficult to reconcile is that the development of leukaemia following whole body irradiation can be greatly reduced (see Fig. 32) if a very small fraction of the total bone-marrow is shielded during irradiation. The volume shielded would reduce by less than 25 per cent the number of cells exposed, and one would expect that the probability of producing a single cancer mutation should decrease by a like amount, but in fact the leukaemia incidence is reduced virtually to zero by shielding. Treatments given after irradiation do not influence the number of mutations, yet the injection of spleen cells some days after irradiation reduces the percentage of mice which develop leukaemia to less than half. How then can the cancer-producing action of the radiation be explained? The concept of cancer as a somatic mutation is almost certainly correct in its broadest sense, since it is only a restatement of the firmly established fact that the malignant transformation is permanent. What does not appear to be true is that atomic radiations produce cancer by acting directly on the genes of the cells affected. It seems more likely that changes in the irradiated tissue or perhaps changes involving the body as a whole – like radiation sickness – make it possible for cells to undergo by themselves the irreversible transformation to malignancy. These experiments emphasize the interdependence of the various healthy cells in a complex organism, and the effects of irradiation on a particular cell cannot be considered in isolation. This may explain the difference between localized and whole body irradiation.

CHAPTER 6

PROTECTION

UNDOUBTEDLY the best way of avoiding the harmful effects of atomic radiations is by surrounding all sources with suitable materials which completely absorb the radiations, and references to protection almost invariably imply screening by purely physical means. Since the radiations are usually highly penetrating, every part is fully accessible to them irrespective of constitution, and in the strict sense protection can be obtained only by excluding the radiations by physical means. At first sight it would therefore appear that taking a chemical substance, such as a drug, before irradiation would be as futile as expecting an aspirin tablet to shield one against a bullet. It is unquestionably true that on exposure to radiations nothing but physical shielding can prevent their passage through the body and that a certain amount of energy will be deposited in every cell. But it must be remembered that the biological changes do not follow directly on the deposition of the energy, and it may be possible to influence the development of the injury at one of the many stages between this first physical step and the appearance of harmful effects. The idea of administering a chemical substance as a prophylactic measure which will reduce the effect of radiation is therefore not as irrational as it appeared at first, and independently groups of researchers working in the U.S.A., Belgium, and Britain reported in 1949 and 1950 that they had discovered protective compounds. When these were injected into mice immediately before irradiation the animals survived a dose of radiation which without chemical protection would have killed them. Since the number of different chemical substances which could be tried as protectors is virtually unlimited it is necessary to have a working theory to determine which compounds to test. The theories which guided the research work in the three laboratories were quite different, and consequently they tested quite different substances. The result was that a number of chemical compounds completely unrelated in constitution were found to possess the ability to protect mammals against radiations. Probably none of the various theories is correct; but they served their purpose by directing attention to active substances.

The stage seemed to be all set five years ago for 'pills against the atom bomb', and world-wide research was started to find radiation protectors which were more effective than those revealed in the first experiment. In addition to possible military and civil defence uses, protective substances could be useful as an adjunct to radiotherapy, and this stimulated studies in cancer research laboratories. All this research revealed that a surprisingly large number of compounds possess the ability to increase to some extent the resistance of mammals to the more acute manifestations of atomic radiations. All the substances work only if given before irradiation, and have no effect whatsoever if administered afterwards, even if only seconds have elapsed. Moreover, the protectors are more active within a few minutes of the radiation, and only one or two can be taken as long as an hour beforehand. The first protector, cysteine,* is a relatively common substance and is present in a bound form in almost all proteins. The Belgian scientist Z. M. Bacq played a most prominent part in the search for protective agents, and found a compound to which he gave the name Becaptan† which has substantial practical advantages

* Cysteine has the structure $NH_2.CH.COOH$ (with $CH_2.SH$ attached below the CH) and is incorporated in proteins with other amino-acids as follows:

$$
\begin{array}{ccccc}
-\,NH.\underset{\substack{|\\ R}}{CH}.CO.NH.\underset{\substack{|\\ CH_2-SH}}{CH}.CO.NH.\underset{\substack{|\\ R'}}{CH}.CO.-
\end{array}
$$

other amino-acid — cysteine — other amino-acid

† Becaptan or β-mercapto-ethylamine has the formula:

$$NH_2.CH_2.CH_2.SH.$$

over cysteine although the actual amount of protection which it gives is no greater. It is both a disappointment and surprise that in spite of the great efforts which have been made, no substance has yet been found which is more effective than cysteine, the very first compound ever to be tried for this purpose.

The simplest way of testing substances for protective action is to inject each into a group of about ten animals, usually mice, which are then irradiated with a dose of X-rays which is just large enough to kill them all within two or three weeks. A feeble protector will prevent three to four out of the ten mice which have been irradiated from dying, while a good protector should save all the animals or certainly nine out of ten. In a typical experiment all the untreated animals died between the fourth and tenth days following irradiation, while of those that had received 3 mg. (or one ten thousandth part of an ounce) of Becaptan all survived. At first sight it might appear as if the problem had been solved, as all the animals lived, but in reality the amount of protection is not very great since the response to radiation is extremely sharp; if 700 r is lethal, 500 r will

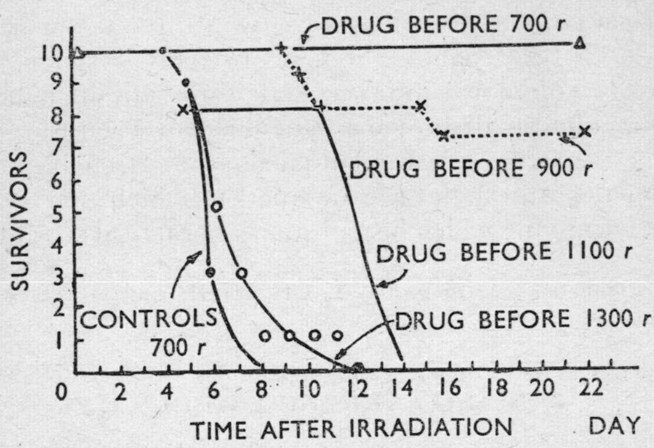

Fig. 33 – Protection of mice by injecting Becaptan before irradiation by X-rays with 700 r, 900 r, 1,100 r, and 1,300 r respectively.

kill, on average, only one or two out of a test group of ten animals. Thus complete protection against a dose which is just sufficient to kill may represent only quite a small increase in resistance to radiation. This is clearly brought out in Fig. 33, where Becaptan, completely effective at 700 r, protects much less against 900 r; at 1,100 r all the treated animals die although death occurs a few days later than without the drug. With a dose of 1,300 r the drug is completely ineffective and the animals die at the same rate as those which receive no protector. The best agents given at

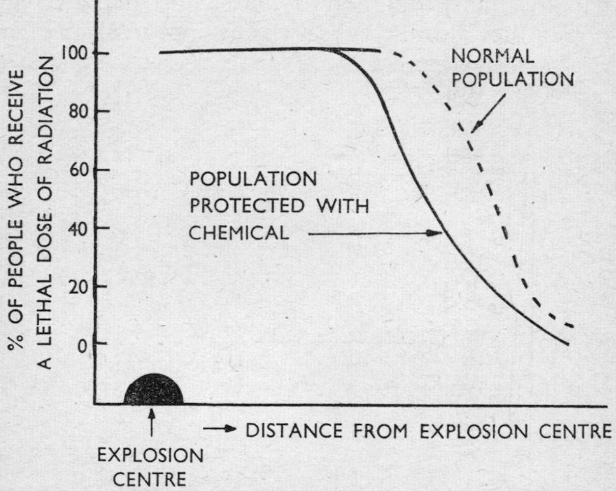

Fig. 34 – Incidence of death from radiation sickness at different distances from an atom bomb, for a population which had taken no chemical protective substance, and for a population which had received maximum chemical protection.

the highest dose tolerated by the animal reduce the effectiveness of the radiations by between one-third and a half. Fig. 34 shows that this amount of protection would not greatly alter the lethality from an atom bomb even if all those exposed had the presence of mind to swallow a pill immediately before the bomb fell. In nuclear war we do not want presence of mind but absence of body! Happily this book is not concerned with military considerations, and from a scientific point of view chemical protection is of the greatest interest as it may help to elucidate the basic mechanisms of radiation injury.

CAN CHEMICALS PROTECT AGAINST ALL THE HARMFUL EFFECTS?

As already pointed out, the protectors cannot reduce the amount of radiation actually received, but they raise the animal's resistance and thereby enable it to survive a bigger dose. Can they also increase the resistance to all the mani-

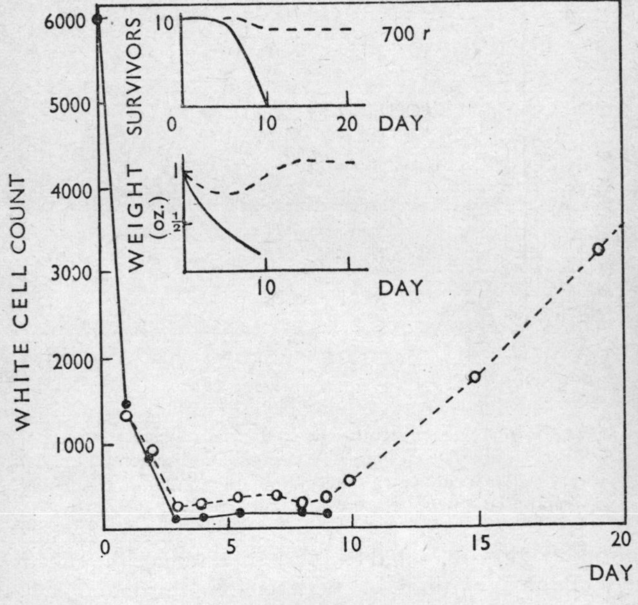

Fig. 35 – Effect of protective agent (Becaptan) on blood count and weight loss of mice which had received a dose sufficient to kill all the controls (700 r).

festations of radiation sickness and do the chemicals protect against the long-term effects? No answer can as yet be given to the second question. Technical difficulties make it extremely hard to measure accurately the number of mutations produced in mammals and no studies have yet been completed to assess the influence of protectors. With the favourite material of geneticists, the fruit-fly, neither cysteine nor Becaptan reduced the mutagenic action of X- and γ-rays, but this experiment is not decisive, since it is possible that the drugs do not reach the reproductive organs. Unlike radiations, chemicals will accumulate selectively in certain organs and be almost completely absent in

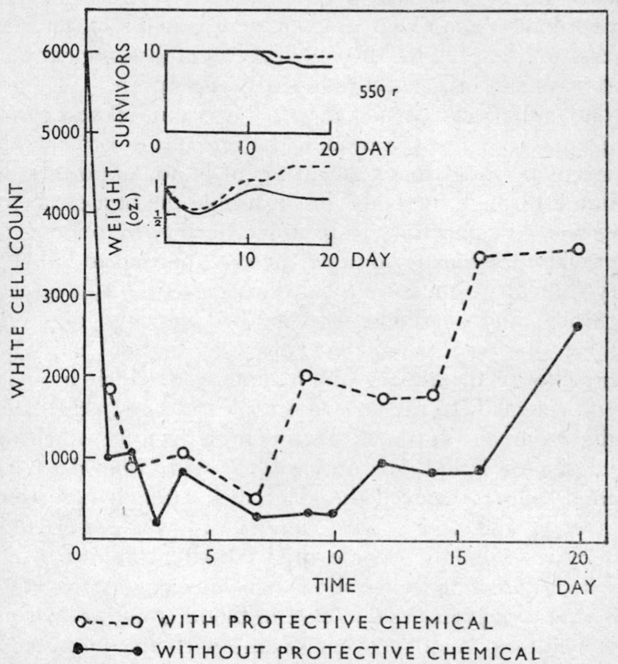

Fig. 36 – Effect of protective agent (Becaptan) on blood count and weight loss after 550 r which produces radiation sickness but virtually no deaths even in the unprotected animals.

others, and selective protection can therefore occur. The number of mutations produced in bacteria can be greatly reduced if they are irradiated in a solution containing protectors, but from this we cannot conclude that chemical protection is possible in higher organisms, the genetic apparatus of which may be quite different from that of unicellular organisms.

In general, there is a direct correlation between breaking of chromosomes and induction of mutations, but again the data for protection against chromosome breaks are conflicting, though in a number of cases some reduction is obtained if suitable chemicals are given beforehand. The cancer-producing action has not been protected against, but the experiments done so far are not very conclusive, and it is interesting that the incidence of cataract following exposure to X-rays can be greatly reduced by Becaptan.

The end-effects associated with radiation sickness can all be protected against, although the amount of protection is different because the chemical agent is not uniformly distributed through the body. For example the best protectors raise the dose necessary to produce sterility by only 30 per cent while they nearly double the dose needed to kill. It is very difficult to measure local damage with any degree of accuracy, and consequently very little, if any, difference can be observed by microscopic examination of various tissues between animals which have and which have not been protected. In the first days after irradiation the extent of tissue damage appears to be the same in mice which had been given a lethal dose and will die within ten days, and animals which received the same dose after being given a protector, and which will therefore all survive. Definite differences will only become apparent after four or five days when the protected mice show signs of recovery from such radiation symptoms as decrease in blood count and weight loss, while no such recovery occurs with the unprotected mice, which will all die a few days later. This is brought out in Fig. 35 which compares the behaviour of protected and non-protected animals. The effect of protective agents when a non-lethal dose is given can be seen from Fig. 36. Without a protector 80 per cent of the animals recover from a dose of 550 r, yet their blood count initially dropped to almost the same extent as after 700 r when no recovery occurred and all the animals died. By comparing Figs. 35 and 36 we see that there is little difference within the first few days in the blood of animals which had received 550 r and 700 r, and one would therefore not expect to detect the action of a protective agent by blood counts within the first week after irradiation.

That protective agents also lower the harm done by doses not sufficient to kill is seen in Fig. 36, when the protected animals recovered earlier. But these experiments do not tell us whether the protective agent lowers the amount of damage to individual organs and thereby decreases the total impact on the system, or whether the chemicals protect only a few centres which are particularly important for recuperation. This last explanation is unlikely, since the same substances which protect animals also reduce the radiation injury in individual cells in tissue culture and unicellular organisms such as bacteria. Moreover, very careful examination shortly after irradiation of some radiosensitive organs, such as the spleen or liver, shows that less damage is produced if a protector is given first. These effects on individual organs can as a rule only be found with relatively small doses, since near the lethal dose the proportion of the cells killed is so high that small differences cannot be detected. For example, it may be that 700 r kills 99 per cent of all the cells in the bone-marrow, while with a protector present only 95 per cent are affected. This small difference could probably not be detected microscopically, yet it could well represent the difference between recovery and death, since with 5 per cent of surviving cells the blood-forming agents may be repopulated with cells in time (i.e. about five days), while in the absence of the protector restoration is too slow for the animal to recover.

The amount of radiation which can be given to a tumour in a patient is usually limited by the amount of damage done to ordinary tissue which is necessarily irradiated at the same time. Modern techniques keep this exposure to a minimum, but some is unavoidable, particularly with deep-seated tumours or when the cancer is disseminated. A real advantage would be obtained if an agent could be found which does not accumulate in the cancer, while protecting the healthy tissue. Unfortunately with the substances so far tried, such as Becaptan, the tumours are also made more radio-resistant. With regard to their general mode of action it is probably safe to conclude that the protective agents reduce the immediate harmful effects of radiation (that is, all the manifestations of radiation sickness) by increasing the resistance of all the individual cells concerned. Since they protect almost all forms of life against X- and γ-rays, this indicates that the action in mammals is also at the level of individual cells and not via some indirect process, such as changes in hormone excretion, which produce changes in other organs. This view is reinforced by the observation that these drugs only work – whatever the system, mouse or bacteria! – if given before irradiation. They have no effect whatever when given afterwards. Before the different possible mechanisms of protection can be discussed it is necessary to describe the influence of oxygen on radiosensitivity.

THE OXYGEN EFFECT

The changes produced by X- and γ-rays in all kinds of living matter are much greater in the presence than in the absence of oxygen. The radiosensitivity depends on the amount of oxygen present, and from Fig. 37 it can be seen that it reaches its limiting value when this is the same as in air. Enriching the normal atmosphere with oxygen does not increase sensitivity, but removal of oxygen from the air decreases it. For the majority of systems studied the radiosensitivity is increased two to three times by changing from an oxygen-free atmosphere to air. That means that if a certain change is produced by 100 r in air, then 200–300 r will be necessary to achieve the same effect in the absence

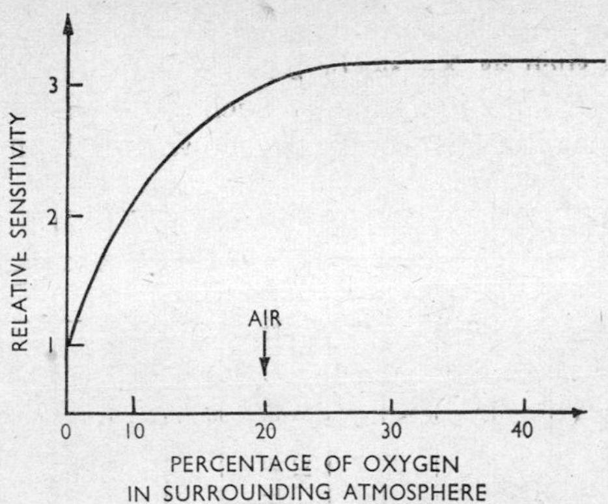

Fig. 37 – Relationship between the oxygen concentration in the atmosphere and the radiation sensitivity for different tissues.

of oxygen. The remarkable feature of this oxygen effect is its universality; it applies equally to the lethal dose for animals, the production of chromosome breaks in bean root or pollen grains, the killing of tumour cells or bacteria, and the production of mutations in fruit-flies.

There are two schools of thought about the mechanism: the presence of oxygen modifies the primary chemical changes produced by radiation possibly in the way discussed on p. 188; or the presence of oxygen influences the metabolic processes necessary for the development of the minute initial chemical change into the observed injury. No crucial experiments have been made to distinguish unambiguously between these possibilities, but the chemical theory seems the more plausible, since it is unlikely that all the different organisms use similar metabolic pathways for developing the observed injuries. Moreover, the oxygen must be present during the irradiation itself, and the radio-sensitivity is unaffected by changes in oxygen immediately after irradiation. Since it takes some time for the injury to develop, one would expect on the metabolic theory that oxygen would be needed after irradiation. More decisive still is the fact that an oxygen effect is only observed with sparsely ionizing radiations such as X-, γ-, or β-rays. The biological effect from densely ionizing radiations such as α-rays or neutrons is independent of oxygen. This is shown clearly in Fig. 38,

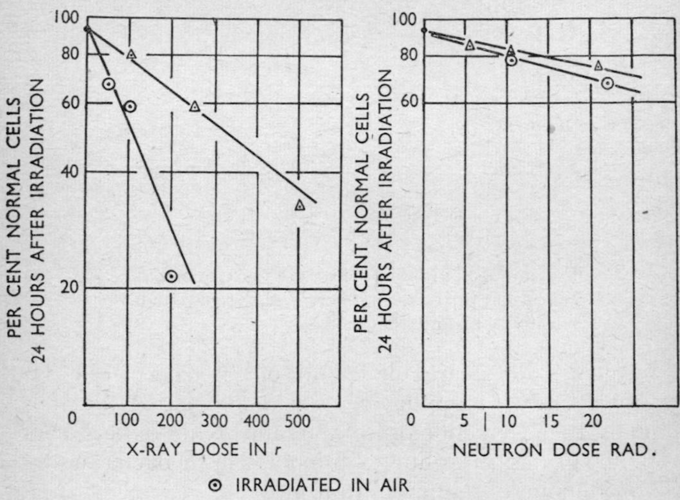

Fig. 38 – Effect of X-rays and neutrons on tumour (ascites) cells, in the presence and absence of oxygen.

which also illustrates the greater effectiveness of the densely ionizing neutrons (for discussion of the relative biological effectiveness of different radiations see p. 206). The failure of densely ionizing radiations to show an oxygen effect follows directly from the chemical theory (see p. 188) and would be difficult to understand if oxygen came into the picture through a metabolic process.

HOW DO CHEMICALS PROTECT?

By analogy with antidotes to poisons the suggestion presents itself that protectors reconstitute some vital molecules or enzymes which, when they are damaged by radiations, give rise to the observed injury. For example, cysteine can restore certain enzymes after they have been inactivated by irradiation in the test tube. However, these particular enzymes are not involved in the initial radiation effect (see p. 212) and repair of any of these molecules cannot bring about protection. A more attractive mechanism is that the protective chemicals lower the oxygen concentration in the irradiated organism either by combining with oxygen in the surrounding fluid (this could apply to bacteria), or by causing some physiological action to occur in the body which results in lowering the amount of oxygen dissolved in the blood. It is of course the blood which ensures that all the tissues are fully aerated. This theory finds support in the fact that the change in radio-sensitivity by chemical protection and by removal of oxygen is of the same magnitude and that chemical protection, like the oxygen effect, is only found with sparsely ionizing radiations and not with neutrons or α-rays. It is very likely that some of the chemical protectors work in this way, but deprivation of oxygen cannot explain the activity of the many highly protective substances, since they do not all have the property of lowering oxygen concentration. Indeed, the active substances have no pharmacological action in common, but all of them compete very effectively for highly reactive chemical entities which are produced when water is irradiated, and consideration of the chemical effects of radiations leads to a mechanism which provides quite logically for protection and the oxygen effect. This is discussed in detail in Chapter 8. The universality of both oxygen effect and chemical protection demands that their action occur at the initial chemical level, since the subsequent biological processes are quite different in the various systems which have been studied.

THE PERFECT PROTECTOR

In spite of much research the protective agents found so far are of very limited usefulness, and it would seem that we have not yet found the optimum step at which to interfere with the radiation process. The known agents probably work by sidetracking some of the energy deposited by radiation into chemical changes which are harmless to the cell. Thereby the harmful impact of a given dose is reduced. An alternative and possibly a more useful approach would be to have chemicals which repair or reconstitute the few vital centres which when damaged by the radiation lead to the observed end effects. But this is the stage about which we have least information, and until we know the nature of these vital centres (see p. 213) this approach to protection cannot be followed. Probably the greatest promise for mitigating the effect of radiations lies in the treatment of the observed injuries and in stimulating the natural recovery processes. What has been done so far along these lines forms the subject of the next chapter.

CHAPTER 7

RECOVERY AND TREATMENT

One of the most characteristic features of all living things is their ability to recover from injuries, and this applies equally to the repair of physical damage and to recuperation from poisoning or illness. One of the most serious aspects of radiation is that it can produce some harmful effects which cannot be reversed – these were discussed in Chapter 4 – although complete recovery occurs from most of the immediately obvious injuries which were discussed under the heading of radiation sickness.

THE TIME FACTOR

The influence on the extent of the injury of the rate at which the dose is given suggests that a number of competing processes go on at the same time in an irradiated organism, whether that is a single cell or a whole animal. In general, the same amount of harm is done by a whole body dose independent of time, so long as the irradiation time is less than an hour or so. For example, the dose necessary to kill a mouse is the same whether it is given at a rate of 10 r/min.– when the irradiation takes about an hour – or in a one-second exposure at 36,000 r/min. If the dose rate is less than a few roentgen per minute, then the total dose needed to kill goes up, and with a dose of 10 r/day the animals must be irradiated for more than a year before they have accumulated a lethal dose (see Fig. 17); it means the dose necessary to kill has been raised from 700 r to 4,500 r by decreasing the dose rate. When the dose rate is reduced to about 1 r per day irradiation will not significantly shorten the life of animals with a life expectancy of less than ten years, although long-term effects still occur.

Dose rate is of similar importance in damage to individual

cells, such as delay in mitosis or chromosome breaks, and even for localized symptoms such as reddening of the skin (see p. 104). What happens is that the body attempts to repair the damage as it occurs, but it requires a certain time to do this – a few days in the case of mammals – and if the irradiation time is less than a few hours no recovery will have taken place during the time of exposure to the radiation. An irradiation is lethal if the amount of damage present at any one time exceeds a certain value, and the animal will die a few days after it has been received, probably because the recovery processes are overwhelmed. If the dose rate is high all the damage piles up and the critical level is reached before any significant amount of restitution has had a chance to occur, and under these conditions the lethal dose is lowest. The processes of restoration vary, so that time for recuperation will be different in different animals and in isolated cells, and this means that the effect of changing dose rate will not be the same in all the different systems studied. When an effect is independent of dose rate no recovery occurs, and the damage by the radiation is completely cumulative. This is the case for the production of mutations, and the same number are produced by a certain dose whether this is given over seconds or years.

When the rate of restoration is equal to or greater than the rate of damage (this is determined by the dose rate) no net injury should result, however long the radiation is applied. This is not the case, since restoration is never quite complete, so that some permanent damage always remains; this is responsible for the shortening of the life-span that has been observed after doses which do not kill immediately. The deaths which occur after exposure to 10 r per day for more than a year are due to the accumulation of this irreparable damage beyond a critical value. Probably about four-fifths of all the harmful effects are reversed, but about one-fifth remain as permanent defects which lower the inherent resistance of the animal. This is clearly shown in experiments where the radiation dose is fractionated; animals are given an irradiation which is not sufficient to kill them, and some time afterwards the dose necessary to kill them is measured. For example, mice with an LD50 (for definition see p. 76) of 700 r are given 400 r, which kills none of them within thirty days; if the second irradiation is given two days later the LD50 will be 500 r (that is, the total dose is 400 r + 500 r, or 200 r higher than the LD50 for a single dose) implying that half of the damage of the initial exposure was repaired in the interval between the irradiations. If the animals are left for a long time between irradiations, then the LD50 for the second dose will be about 620 r, and this will be the same whether the interval is one month or one year. Since this is 80 r less than the LD50 for a single dose, this suggests that one-fifth (or 80 r) of the initial 400 r was not repaired.

Normal metabolism is necessary both for developing the radiation injury (see p. 67) and for the subsequent repair processes, and the effect of varying the time factors is therefore not always easy to disentangle. Restoration has been studied by an elegant method with eggs of the silkworm which will no longer hatch after a dose of about 1,500 r. By fractionation, restoration processes were shown to occur at ordinary room temperature as follows: two separate irradiations of 1,000 r each with an interval of one day during which the eggs are left at room temperature will not prevent the eggs from hatching. If the eggs were stored at low temperatures between the irradiations, however, then no eggs would hatch. The explanation is that the major part of the damage from the first 1,000 r was repaired when the eggs were stored at room temperature, but in the cold the metabolic activity was too low to cause repair between irradiations – just as it is too low to develop up the injuries from the primary chemical damage (see p. 179) – so that after the second dose the accumulated damage was sufficient to prevent hatching.

PROMOTING RESTORATION

The American scientist Alexander Hollaender has achieved considerable success in increasing survival of bacteria by treatments which promote restoration. For example, the temperature at which the bacteria are stored after irradiation very greatly influences their survival, and Fig. 39 shows that if they are allowed to stand for a few hours at a

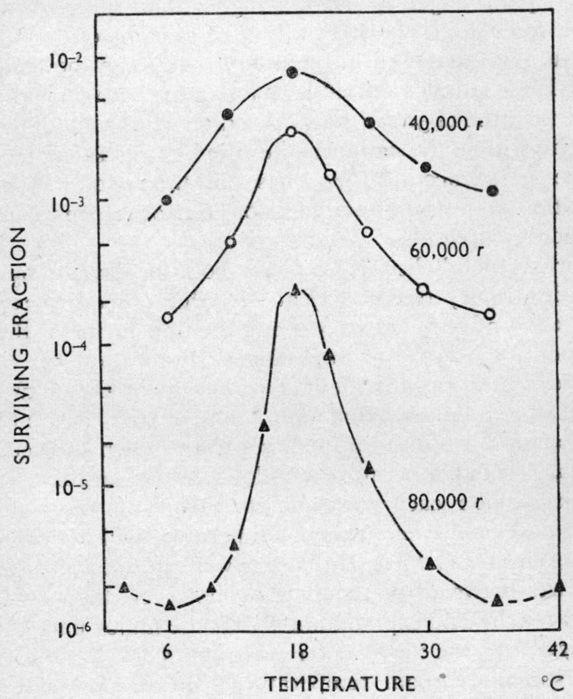

Fig. 39 – Increase in survival of bacteria (*E. coli* B/r) by storing at 18° C (64° F) after irradiation.

temperature below that at which they grow best, more survive; but if the temperature is too low the value of the after-treatment is lost. There are two opposing metabolic processes at work; those which develop the injury and those which restore the damage. Both these processes will be reduced by lowering the temperature, but it would appear as if the one giving rise to damage is decreased to a greater extent than the one responsible for recovery, so that the net effect of cooling is beneficial. The addition of certain specific nutrients (one might call them vitamins) to the medium on which bacteria are grown after the irradiation also increases survival. No substance or post-treatment has so far been found which stimulates the recuperative powers of more complex organisms such as animals, although there are indications that some such substances exist and are released during irradiation; their isolation and identification is probably only a matter of time.

For assisting recovery of mammals another approach, that of replacing a critically damaged organ, has been most successful. The clue how this could be done came from experiments designed to find out why irradiation of the whole body was so much more dangerous than exposing a part only (see Table IV, p. 75). Careful work showed that resistance was greatly increased by shielding from irradiation some of the sites at which the blood is formed (the haematopoietic organs). The most important blood-forming centre is the bone-marrow, and this explains why shielding such apparently unimportant parts of an animal as the tail is already sufficient to increase the lethal dose by 50 per cent. Another important organ is the spleen, and if this remains unexposed then the rest of the animal can receive nearly twice the dose before death occurs.

These experiments suggest that implantation of a spleen after radiation may increase the chance of survival, and this did in fact prove to be the case. Tissue grafting is only successful between very closely related animals; it is well known that in plastic surgery only the patient's own skin can be used; any other would not take. The only exception is identical twins, between whom exchange is possible. The spleen-grafting experiments had therefore to be done with a completely inbred strain of mice, all of which can be considered as alike as identical twins. It would at first sight appear as if these experiments were of academic interest only, since no such 'inbred' material would be available for the treatment of human beings. The next step was to see if the whole organ was necessary or whether injection of a cell suspension from an unirradiated spleen would promote recovery. The attempt was strikingly successful, and this very simple procedure brought about complete recovery from a lethal dose by a treatment given after irradiation. Cells from the bone-marrow work equally well and offer some technical advantages over spleen cells.

Is this recovery due to the cell grafting? That is, do the injected cells settle and repopulate the irradiated organs or do they merely provide some very special substance which promotes recovery? There seemed to be a decisive experiment which would give the answer; if only suspensions from the same inbred mouse strain gave recovery, then the effect would probably be due to grafting by intact cells. On the other hand, if cells from other mouse strains could be used, then the active factor was some substance – one might call it a hormone – contained in the cell. The answer was quite definite; not only could spleen or bone-marrow cells from any mouse be used, but even guinea-pig and rat cells promoted recovery of an irradiated mouse and the conclusion seemed inescapable that a chemical factor was involved, and recovery was promoted by it in the same way as special nutrients assist bacteria to recover. It only remained to isolate the substance, and then there would be a drug which would promote recovery, and whose usefulness would extend far beyond the treatment of radiation injuries. In spite of intensive research no completely cell-free extract was found active, and any process which killed the cells or broke them up also inactivated the suspension. Even storage for an hour was sufficient to reduce the potency. Here was a paradox; living whole cells are necessary, but these can be taken from unrelated animals, and according to all the laws of immunology they cannot grow as a graft. What reason other than the need to grow and multiply can there be why living cells are so essential?

AN ALIEN BLOOD SUPPLY

The answer was found in 1955 by a group under Dr J. F. Loutit in the medical unit attached to the atomic research centre at Harwell. It was simple; the laws of immunology do not apply to the special case of the irradiated mammal. If a mouse of strain A is irradiated and then given an injection of cells from a mouse of strain B, all the cells in the bone-marrow of A become of the type typical for strain B. The key to this discovery was the development of a new technique which enabled the cells from mice of different strains to be distinguished. This was achieved as a by-product of studying the genetic effects of radiations; a mutation was produced in which one of the chromosomes had been distinguishably altered in shape. Every cell which has one of these must be derived from cells originating in a mouse from this one mutant strain. When ordinary mice were injected after irradiation with bone-marrow from the special mutant strain, all the cells in the blood-forming organs contained this sickle-shaped chromosome. This concept was extended, and it was found that even rat cells would take and multiply in irradiated mice. The mouse had become a chimaera – the mythological monster with a lion's head, a goat's body and a serpent's tail. This word has been used in botany to describe plants such as an apple tree with a pear branch, but only radiation has made it possible to achieve these mixtures in animals.

The reason why foreign cells can completely take over certain organs in irradiated organisms is probably the result of two co-operative factors. The blood-forming organs are particularly sensitive to radiation and most of the cells are killed by relatively small doses and the sites are therefore ready for repopulation by new cells. Radiation also temporarily represses the normal response of the body to foreign cells. The immune reactions, which in a healthy animal immediately throw out any foreign cells, function only sluggishly after irradiation (see p. 100) and the injected cells have a chance to establish themselves in a favourable environment. Even so, the discovery that the injected cells flourish and effectively replace a damaged organ is a historic finding which clearly heralds the day of the prolongation of life, since it has removed the apparently insurmountable obstacle of immunological incompatibility which stood in the way of replacing worn-out organs by other ones.

CHAPTER 8

ENTER THE CHEMIST

THE steps involved between exposure to radiation and the first detectable indications of radiation injury can be formulated in general terms, and have been referred to above (see p. 68). The first step is the uptake of energy from the subatomic particles or radiations, and the principles underlying this process are well understood. The mere deposition of energy in a cell cannot initiate the processes which lead to the observed end-effects; the energy must bring about some chemical change which modifies some cell constituents. The energy not used for chemical reactions becomes available as heat, but this cannot be responsible for any of the biological changes, since the dose of radiation sufficient to kill a man (500 r) is only capable of raising his temperature by just over one thousandth part of a degree, which is much less than the every-day variations.

By determining the type of chemical reactions which ionizing radiations produce and the processes by which the energy is converted into chemical change the chemist plays an important part in the unfolding story of the biological effects of ionizing radiations. The observed end-effects are various and complex, as was seen in the previous chapters, and it is very difficult to deduce from these the nature of the initial injuries which they arouse. Only after a closer understanding of these early steps has been obtained will a less empirical approach be possible to the problems of radiobiology, such as improving radiation therapy, protecting against and treating radiation injuries. The rapidly expanding field of radiation chemistry can throw new light on the chemical changes produced, and thereby provide a new approach to the problem from a new direction. Quite apart from the biological implications, some of the chemical changes produced are of practical importance, and the modification of the properties of plastics by irradiation is already being used by industry. The chemical use of ionizing radiations may be as important an adjunct to the production of power from atomic processes as is the extraction of valuable chemicals from the tarry residues in the manufacture of coal gas. The great fascination of studying the chemical effects is that the implications are so varied and often so unpredictable.

Macromolecules. Much is known about the nature of the different substances which occur in living matter, and biochemists are rapidly unravelling their function. Essentially they may be classified into low molecular weight compounds with molecules containing only a few atoms, and high molecular weight compounds in which an individual molecule contains tens of thousands of atoms. This division is not clear-cut, but in practice there are relatively few intermediate compounds. Both classes are vital to life, and it is no more possible for a muscle to function without the small molecule universally known as ATP, which provides the energy or fuel for the contraction, than without the macromolecule myosin which makes up the fibres which perform the work. Yet there are good reasons for the belief that the biologically important chemical changes produced by ionizing radiations are those involving macromolecules, since the amount of energy which most biological systems have to take up before they are injured is only capable of affecting a relatively small number of atoms. A chemical change which may affect the biological function of the whole molecule usually follows a change produced by irradiation in a single one of its constituent atoms, and as a first approximation it can be assumed that a given dose of atomic rays will produce a change in the same number of molecules whether they be large or small. Since there are many more small than large molecules, a certain amount of radiation will change (inactivate?) a much greater *proportion* of all the macromolecules than of the small molecules. In other words, the same dose may cause a harmful decrease in some large molecules but an entirely insignificant change in the total number of small molecules. For example, in order to work, a muscle requires both intact myosin and ATP, but there are many hundred times as many small ATP molecules as large myosin molecules. Simply for illustration let us consider a system containing an equal weight of ATP and myosin, and let us assume that irradiation can render ATP useless as an energy source and damage the myosin molecule, thereby interfering with the mechanical properties essential to the muscle fibre. In this hypothetical assembly there will be 200 times as many ATP molecules of molecular weight 300 as of myosin molecules with molecular weight 60,000. Now a dose of radiation sufficient to change one atom in each myosin molecule will only put out of action 1 out of 200 of the ATP molecules. Our imaginary muscle will fail to function because ionizations in the myosin molecules have damaged the fibre and not because of the insignificant decrease in the energy supply due to the loss of 0·5 per cent of ATP.

DIRECT AND INDIRECT ACTION

The uptake of energy from ionizing radiations is largely independent of the chemical constitution of the material irradiated (see p. 25) and no serious error will be introduced by assuming that equal weights of the diverse materials in the body, including water, take up the same amount of energy from a given dose of radiation. Most living systems contain a great deal of water, which may make up as much as 85 per cent of the weight of a mammal, consequently on irradiation of an animal most of the energy will initially be deposited in water and only a small proportion will be taken up by the materials which make up the body, such as the skin, bones, muscles, etc., and by the solids dissolved in the body fluids such as the proteins in blood. The energy taken up in the water is not wasted since it 'activates' water molecules which then react with dissolved substances or other materials with which they come into contact. Changes produced by the reaction of activated water molecules are referred to as 'indirect' action of radiation in contrast to 'direct' action which applies to those changes which occur in the material which initially absorbs the radiation.*

Some living things, such as seeds and bacterial spores, can be dried without being killed, and if they are irradiated in the absence of water, direct action only can occur. In most cases, however, both direct and indirect action will take place, and it becomes a matter of some importance to decide whether the chemical changes initiating the biological injury were brought about by activated water or by energy deposited within the material itself. Until recently it had been considered that external factors could not influence a process due to direct action, as it was believed that once a molecule had taken up the necessary amount of energy certain chemical changes were bound to occur, and the course of this reaction could not be stopped or interfered with in any way. The activated water molecule has to travel some distance before it can react, and during this process it can be captured by another substance. Neighbouring materials can change the course of indirect action and the addition of a compound which reacts readily with activated water may act as a protector since it will capture some of the activated water molecules before they come into contact with a biologically important material. Other substances, notably oxygen, can combine with activated water to produce a still more reactive entity which will be more destructive and the indirect action of radiation will therefore be enhanced. Another way of influencing indirect action is to

* Some confusion has arisen by the use of the term *direct* for those biological changes which occur at the site of irradiation, and *indirect* for those injuries which are seen in a part of the animal which has never been exposed to radiation. Many instances of this kind have been studied (see p. 39), and their occurrence in radiotherapy is occasionally a serious complication. The use of the terms direct and indirect for events on the molecular level, as defined here, has become almost universal and in consequence they should not be used for systemic biological effects; for these the term 'action at a distance' is to be preferred.

interfere with the movement of the activated water by freezing; in this case the activated water is prevented from coming into contact with the substance it would otherwise attack.

Since many of the biological effects of radiation can be modified to some extent by external factors (such as protective agents and changes in oxygen concentration, see Chap. 6) it is believed that indirect action plays an important role; this, of course, one might have expected in view of the high water content in animals and most living cells. The contribution of direct action cannot be neglected and may, indeed, be more important than the preponderance of water suggests; this will be discussed on p. 202.

WHAT IS ACTIVATED WATER?

It has been known for many years that dilute solutions of a large variety of substances in water are chemically changed on irradiation and that the amount of the dissolved material which reacted was independent of its concentration. On exposing solutions of alcohol, this decomposes, and one of the products is the gas hydrogen: the volume of this gas produced depends only on the radiation dose, and is the same for a 0·1 per cent as for a 1 per cent solution. This behaviour can only be understood if the action is indirect; that is if the activated water attacks the alcohol and thereby liberates hydrogen gas, since the number of such activated entities produced will be the same in a solution containing 0·1 per cent as 1 per cent of alcohol. If the change occurred as a result of the direct energy uptake by the alcohol molecules, the amount of gas produced would be ten times greater in the 1 per cent than in the 0·1 per cent solution.

The vague term 'activated water' is no longer used since we now know more precisely what happens when water is irradiated. In recent years much effort has been devoted to solving this problem and the general pattern is well understood, although details remain to be solved. A suggestion made as long ago as 1929 by Risse, one of the earliest workers in the field, has now been confirmed; on irradiation water is split up into free radicals:

$$H_2O \longrightarrow H\cdot + OH\cdot$$

These, it will be remembered (see p. 19), are highly reactive entities since they do not have the electron configuration required for stable molecules. They have an odd electron, and to become stable H· must lose an electron to give H^+ (the hydrogen ion) and OH· must gain an electron to become OH^- (the hydroxyl ion); both these ions are very stable and non-reactive. The great reactivity of activated water is due to these radicals, which attack most organic substances so as to attain a normal electron configuration. If these radicals do not find something with which to react they will combine with one another and in solution they persist for less than one-thousandth part of a second.

The free radicals are formed when the ionizing particle (e.g. an electron from a β-ray or an electron liberated on irradiation with X- or γ-rays) in its passage through water ejects an electron to produce a positive ion

$$H_2O \xrightarrow[\text{radiation}]{\text{ionizing}} H_2O^+ + e$$

The electron is then captured by another water molecule to give a negative ion

$$H_2O + e \longrightarrow H_2O^-$$

to complete the formation of an ion pair. Now neither of these ions* is stable, and they decompose almost immediately as follows:

$$H_2O^+ \longrightarrow H^+ + OH\cdot$$
$$H_2O^- \longrightarrow OH^- + H\cdot$$

to give two free radicals and the two stable ions H^+ and OH^-, which recombine to give water.

* These ions are unstable because they are also charged free radicals and are quite different from the stable ions which, although electrically charged, have a stable electronic configuration (see p. 16).

Indirect action can be interpreted satisfactorily in terms of the reaction of H· and OH· radicals formed in water and the attack of these radicals on other substances. These reactions are always in competition with the recombination of the radicals to give back water (H· + OH· $\longrightarrow$ H_2O), hydrogen gas (H· + H· $\longrightarrow$ H_2), or the well-known chemical hydrogen peroxide (OH· + OH· $\longrightarrow$ H_2O_2). The latter is a stable molecule which can nevertheless react with many substances, and its formation within sensitive structures, such as the cell nucleus, could be very harmful; it may therefore contribute to the harmful effects of activated water.

Whether the radicals react with dissolved substances or combine with one another depends on their concentration in the track of the ionizing particle as well as on the concentration and susceptibility to attack of the dissolved material. An estimate can be made of the distribution of the radicals in the tracks of different ionizing particles from records obtained in Wilson cloud chambers. But the data obtained apply only to gases, and as already mentioned (see p. 23) extrapolation from gas to liquid involves some uncertainty, but the general pattern seems pretty certain.*

The concentration of the negative ions which give rise to OH radicals depends on the specific ionization density of the radiation. Electrons emitted from β-ray isotopes or ejected by X- or γ-rays are very sparsely ionizing, so that the concentration of the radicals within the track is very low. With therapy X-rays, for example, it is less than one thousandth of one per cent. Under these conditions recombination of the free radicals is extremely unlikely so long as there is an appreciable quantity of a dissolved substance with which to react.

* The H_2O^+ ions are formed in the track of the particle, but the ejected electron travels some distance before it is captured to give H_2O^-; these are formed as a sheath round the track. The distance which this electron travels is not known; various estimates have been made, and in the subsequent calculation the value of 150Å, chosen by Dr L. H. Gray, has been taken.

With α-particles the position is entirely different; because of the high specific ionization density a central column containing OH radicals in very high concentration is obtained which is surrounded by a more diffuse atmosphere of H radicals. Consequently by far the greater part of the OH radicals will combine with one another to give a concentrated core of hydrogen peroxide and only a small proportion will react with any dissolved material. One might say the effect of α-rays on water and aqueous solutions is equivalent to a number of very fine jets of hydrogen peroxide of about 2 per cent concentration, and it is a subject for conjecture whether the biological effects of α-rays can be attributed to the formation of very small volumes of relatively concentrated peroxide within cells. Although treatment of cells with peroxide for short periods does not produce radiation-like effects, it can be argued that this peroxide cannot penetrate into some parts of the cell, in particular the nucleus, and that α-radiation is the only method of introducing jets of peroxide into these parts.

Because of the recombination of many of the radicals in the tracks, α-rays are much less effective than X- or γ-rays in bringing about by indirect action chemical changes which require free radicals. α-rays have the same order of efficiency as X-rays in reactions which do not need the highly reactive free radicals but can be brought about by hydrogen peroxide. But such processes are not likely to be as important biologically as those which only the free radicals can effect. In model experiments it is often found that important biologically active substances such as enzymes extracted from cells are readily inactivated by free OH radicals, but are not destroyed by short exposure to hydrogen peroxide. Since in most living systems densely ionizing radiations are much more effective than X- or γ-rays it might be concluded that indirect action is relatively unimportant in radiobiology. This conclusion is not necessarily valid, since to produce a biologically damaging effect it may be necessary for a number of radicals to react close together and the chance of multiple action occurring will be smaller with X-rays where the radicals are formed far apart than with α-rays. The greater effectiveness of densely ionizing radiations does, however, exclude the possibility that reactions by isolated OH radicals contribute significantly to the processes which lead to the injuries observed.

Much is now known about the kind of chemical reactions in which these free radicals take part; they may bring about the bridging of two molecules by oxidation of so-called SH groups which are present in most proteins as follows:

$$\Big| -SH + SH- \Big| \xrightarrow{2\ OH\cdot} \Big| -S-S- \Big| + 2\,H_2O$$

one OH radical reacts with one SH group.

Another way in which radicals act is by breaking large molecules into smaller fragments, and some of those reactions can cause the molecule to lose its biological activity, such as enzyme action. But because of their very high reactivity the radicals will react with very many groups which are not essential for their biological function, and such a reaction will consequently not be harmful. In living systems many of the radicals will also react with molecules which are of no great importance to the cell or with small molecules of which there are a very great number. The large majority of the radicals formed when biological materials are irradiated will therefore be wasted in reactions which do not affect the normal functioning of the cell. The great reactivity of the free radicals makes them non-selective in their action and therefore inefficient in bringing about specific chemical changes leading to loss of function. Model experiments using solutions of viruses well illustrate this point. A virus injuring the tobacco plant is known to be inactivated if certain atoms in the giant molecule of which it is composed are changed. Yet it is necessary on the average for about a thousand or more free radicals to react with it before it is inactivated, and most of the radicals are wasted in reactions with the virus that do not lead to inactivation.

THE OXYGEN EFFECT

The sensitivity of almost all biological systems to the action of the radiations of relatively low specific ionization (e.g. therapy X-rays and γ-rays) becomes less as the amount of oxygen present in the surrounding atmosphere is decreased below that contained in air (see p. 166). In most cases it is necessary to give from two to three times the dose to produce the same effect in the complete absence of oxygen as in air, which contains approximately 20 per cent of oxygen. The way in which oxygen enhances the radiation effect could involve either the initial chemical reaction or the subsequent biological processes by which the initial chemical damage is amplified until it is seen as a radiation injury some hours or even days after the irradiation. Although no completely decisive test has yet been made there is much evidence (see p. 167) to indicate that the oxygen enhances the initial damage. This view is supported by the observation that the determining factor is the concentration of oxygen during the irradiation, and changes immediately before or after exposure do not influence radiosensitivity.

Chemical experiments show that oxygen reacts very rapidly with the hydrogen radical formed by the indirect action of radiation to give another radical, HO_2, i.e.

$$H\cdot + O_2 \longrightarrow HO\cdot_2$$

Oxygen also increases the amount of hydrogen peroxide produced by radiations of low specific ionization, and many chemical reactions produced by free radicals in water occur to a greater extent in the presence than in the absence of oxygen. These chemical experiments make it tempting to attribute the effect of oxygen in radiobiology to enhancing the changes produced by indirect action. This mechanism would also explain why oxygen has little influence on the biological action of densely ionizing radiations such as α-particles or fast neutrons which produce radicals at high concentration along their tracks so that the dissolved oxygen cannot effectively intervene to produce HO_2 radicals.

However, this argument is not conclusive, since the chemical changes produced by direct action are also influenced by oxygen and the oxygen effect does not prove that the indirect action of free radicals contributes more than direct action to the important initial changes.

CHEMICAL PROTECTION

The remarkable observation that added chemicals present during irradiation can increase the resistance of cells and whole animals to radiation has been described in Chapter 6. These chemicals, since they are effective only if present during the irradiation, must be considered as protective agents and not as a therapeutic agent which treats the sickness. Protection can occur in one of two ways; the chemical acts on the animal and alters some of its physiological processes in such a way as to make it more radiation-resistant, or the chemical interferes with the primary chemical reaction which initiates the sequence of events leading to radiation injury. The reason why the chemical mechanism seems to be more likely has already been summarized (see p. 167), but its exact nature can, of course, only be understood in terms of radiation chemistry. The amount of energy taken up by an animal on exposure to a dose of radiation cannot, of course, be modified by the protective chemicals; only screening by lead shields or other substances can do this. Nevertheless there are a number of ways by which this energy can be side-tracked so as to reduce damage to vital cell components. When the action is indirect then protection will be found if the added chemical reacts readily with free radicals and competes for them with the vital cell constituents. The extent of the competition will depend on the concentration at which the protective agent is present in those parts of the cell which are most sensitive to radiation (i.e. probably the nucleus) and on the rate at which it reacts with free radicals.

Such protection will, of course, only be effective against damage initiated by indirect action. If the action is direct the energy is deposited immediately within the vital molecules affected, and until recently it was believed that no protection is possible under these circumstances. But in the last few years evidence has been found that energy may in certain circumstances be transferred from the substance which took it up to another material before any chemical changes have occurred, and the possibility exists that added chemicals may protect against direct processes although no evidence has yet been found for this in living systems.

Protection may occur by still a different process if the initial radiation-induced chemical reaction does not immediately damage the important molecules beyond repair. From purely chemical studies a number of cases are known where atomic radiations both by direct and by indirect action change a molecule into an unstable entity which decomposes a very short time later (usually much less than a second), unless another substance is present which repairs the unstable material as soon as it is formed. Formally this method of protection may be represented as follows:

$$\underset{\text{vital macromolecule}}{RH} \xrightarrow{\text{radiation}} \underset{\text{unstable free radical}}{R\cdot} \xrightarrow{\text{decomposes}} \text{product changed irreversibly}$$

In presence of protective agent (PH) the unstable intermediate is converted back to its original state by the following reaction

$$R\cdot + PH \longrightarrow RH + \underset{\text{damaged protective agent}}{P\cdot}$$

and instead the protective chemical is destroyed.

In biological systems it is not possible to find out by which of these three processes the protective agent functions, since the primary chemical changes produced cannot be detected. Valuable indications, however, can be obtained by analogy with protection in simple systems where the chemical steps can be worked out. To do this scientists trained in different disciplines must co-operate – I have taken part in fruitful collaborations of this kind. While studying the effects of irradiation on different materials we found that polymethacrylic acid, a substance of high molecular weight and related to some of the plastics in everyday use, was degraded. Because it was experimentally convenient, solutions of this material in water were used to find out more about the chemical changes produced by indirect action of radiation, and it was noted that the breakdown of this polymer could be prevented by adding to the solution certain other substances which could be considered as protectors of the polymer against radiation. At a scientific meeting I heard an account by Prof. Z. M. Bacq of his work on the protection of mammals against the lethal effect of X-rays by administering chemicals immediately before irradiation. Unexpectedly, the mouse and the polymer responded to the same chemicals, and the similarity between the two systems seemed to be more than coincidence. Collaboration was arranged, and for three years an exciting interchange of samples and information took place. Eventually more than one hundred substances were tested in detail in the mouse and in the polymer, and a close parallelism was established. The same substances were active in the two systems and were, moreover, placed very nearly in the same order of effectiveness. There were, of course, exceptions, but the majority of these could be understood when it was realized that the animal being a living system rapidly metabolizes certain substances which remain unchanged in the solutions containing only polymer.

In the simplified artificial system the mechanism of protection could be determined; the polymer under the conditions of the experiment is degraded by HO_2 radicals formed in aerated water and the added chemicals protected by successfully competing with the polymer molecules for these radicals. In other experiments with model substances the protective power of added substances against OH radicals or by the repair mechanism described on p. 190 were tested, but the protective action of different substances in these systems could not be correlated with that observed in the mouse. Arguing by analogy we concluded the chemicals also protect the mouse by competing for HO_2 radicals and that they protect against that part of radiation damage brought about by these radicals. The following observations made in the animal experiments can readily be understood on the basis of this hypothesis:

(1) Protection occurs only in the presence of oxygen (or air); in the absence of oxygen the HO_2 radical cannot be formed in water.*

(2) Chemicals are ineffective or much less effective in protecting against the effects of radiations such as those from α-particles or protons which give high ion densities. In the tracks of these particles the radical concentration is so high that effective removal by competition becomes impossible.

(3) The amount of protection which can be given by chemicals is limited. A number of substances are all equally active in reducing the action to slightly less than half, but no improvement beyond this has ever been found. This behaviour is to be expected if the chemicals protect against only one of the ways by which radiation damages cells.

Experiments in simple systems quite unrelated to life can be most valuable for finding out the nature of the fundamental primary reactions of radiations in the complex living organism. Even if the working hypothesis for chemical protection, just outlined, should be proved wrong by further experiments, the emphasis in radiobiology research is being placed more and more on obtaining information about the radiochemical processes which take place in the cell. For half a century research has been largely directed to studying the end-effects of irradiation and the anatomical changes produced have been recorded in the closest detail, but it is unlikely that further progress in radiotherapy or in the treatment of the harmful effects will come from continued studies of this kind. The next stage of research is to find out the initial points of attack in biological systems.

Before attempting to correlate the chemical changes pro-

* This does not mean that the whole of the oxygen effect observed generally in radiobiology is due to the formation of HO_2 radicals, although these must play some part in the increased radiosensitivity in air or oxygen.

duced by radiation with the damage to biological systems we must consider an entirely different approach which has been most fruitful in developing the subject. This is known as the target theory, and stresses the statistical distribution of events, such as ionization, which are likely to result in chemical changes without worrying about what they actually are. This treatment, although insufficient by itself to explain the biological effects, has produced some valuable concepts which will have to be incorporated in any comprehensive theory.

CHAPTER 9

HITTING THE TARGET

IN 1924 the English physicist Crowther tentatively put forward the target concept which, until recently, completely dominated thinking about the basic mechanism by which radiobiological changes are brought about. As with most revolutionary concepts the idea behind it is simple; it is assumed that in the cell, or other biological material which is being irradiated, there are one or more sensitive volumes within which either one (called a single-hit process) or several (multi-hit process) ionizations have to occur to bring about the observed effect. The number and distribution of ionizations is assumed to be the same as in gases where it can be measured directly* in the Wilson cloud chamber, and it is postulated that excitations of atoms – which must occur as well as ionizations – are not capable of inactivating the sensitive points.

In theory, it is possible from a fairly limited amount of experimental data to calculate the number of hits required and the size of the sensitive volume. If experiments are done with radiations having different ionization densities, for example, if both X- and α-rays are used, one can calculate whether the sensitive volume – the target – is present as one sensitive centre, or as a number of smaller sites distributed throughout the cell, whose total volume is equal to the target volume. If we consider a bacterium, which requires a single hit for inactivation, then the number put out of action will initially be proportional to the dose, but as the

* Reasons have been given on p. 23 why the number of ionizations produced in liquids or solids cannot be determined directly, and the whole concept of the target theory is based on the assumption that the relative amounts of energy used up in ionizations and excitations is the same for solids, liquids, and gases, and that the energy needed to form an ion pair is also the same. There is no experimental evidence for this last assumption.

process continues larger doses will be needed to bring about further inactivation (see Fig. 40). This comes about because the physical uptake of energy occurs to the same extent in bacteria which have not so far been irradiated as in those

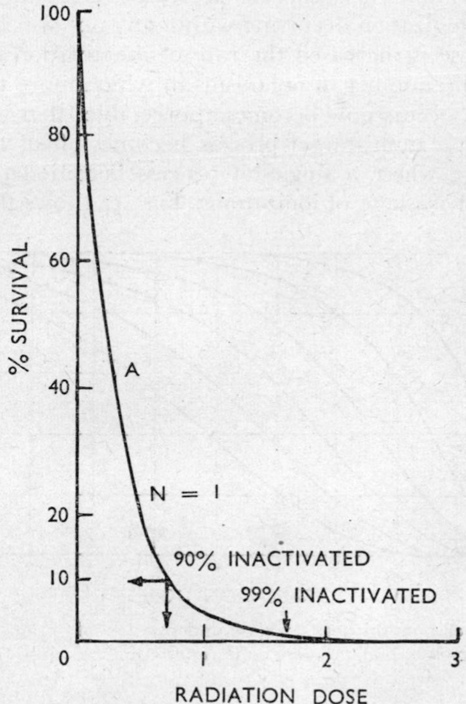

Fig. 40—Relationship between number of organisms inactivated and the dose of X-rays for the case where one hit is sufficient to kill the cell.

already affected; any ionizations occurring in the latter will be wasted, since one hit only is necessary. The proportion of the irradiation lost in this way increases progressively. This is illustrated in Fig. 40, which shows that to increase the proportion of bacteria killed in a preparation from 90 to 99 per cent twice the dose will have to be given.

If more than one target has to be hit to produce inactivation, then the curve relating dose with response will be S-shaped. The reason why small doses are less effective is that when the total number of ionizations is less than the total number of organisms present, the chance of more than one ionization occurring within any one will be small. As the dose is increased the rate of inactivation goes up, because the number of organisms in which more than one ionization occurs now becomes appreciable: that is, inactivation for a multi-target process becomes effective in the dose range where a single-hit process becomes inefficient because of wastage of ionizations. Fig. 41 shows the shape

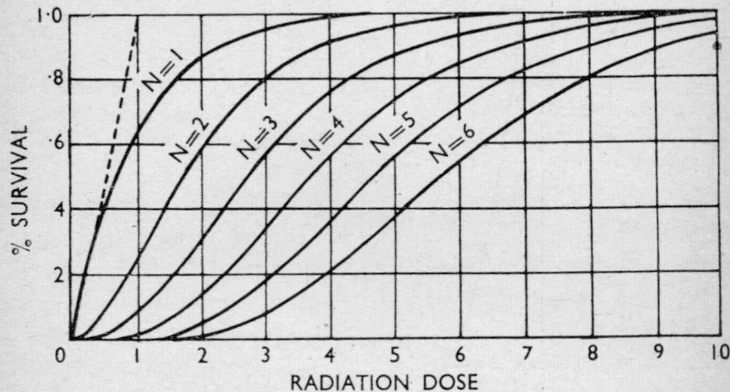

Fig. 41 – Relationship between dose and number of organisms inactivated for cells which require different numbers (N) of hits for inactivation.

of inactivation curves for different processes and from such curves it can be determined how many hits have to be registered per organism to produce the observed effect. From these curves the volume of the sensitive area can also be calculated, since the distribution of the ionizations depends only on the well-known physical characteristics of the radiation used and not at all on the material irradiated. If the dimensions of the target are small compared with the distance between successive ionizations in the track of the subatomic particle, then the problem is simple, and the target volume is proportional to the dose needed to inactivate a certain fraction of the organisms.

For single-hit inactivation densely ionizing radiations are much less effective because when they pass through the target a number of ionizations will occur within it, all but one of which is wasted (see Fig. 42). If the target is large

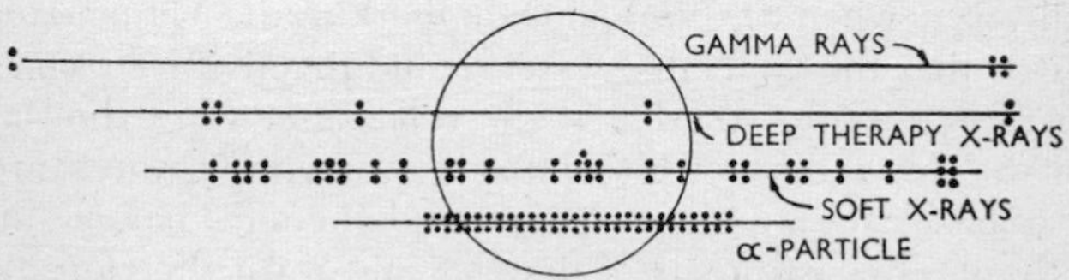

Fig. 42 – Number of ionizations produced in a volume with the size of a small virus by different ionizations. The chance of more than one cluster being formed within it is small for hard radiations but large for α-particles and to a lesser extent for soft X-rays.

then α-rays will be very much less effective (about one-fiftieth) than hard X- or γ-rays, while for smaller targets the difference will be less, but the relative efficiency of α-particles is unlikely ever to exceed one half of that of sparsely ionizing radiations. For multi-hit inactivations the relative effectiveness of different radiations depends on the relative positions of the targets and also on their shape.

A great deal of radiobiological data was examined on the basis of the target theory and values were derived for the sensitive volumes in cells and for the number of hits necessary to inactivate them. In his original paper Crowther calculated the volume which determined whether or not mitosis occurs in an irradiated cell. The value obtained corresponded closely with the apparent size of the centromere – the point at which the chromosomes are attached to the spindle at anaphase (see p. 46) – but we now know that any attempt to identify the sensitive volume with a structure which exists only during mitosis cannot be useful, since cells are not radiosensitive at that stage.

Before the target theory can be applied it must be established that the action is predominantly direct and not brought about by free radicals produced in surrounding water. When the material is dry, as in seeds, the problem does not arise, but most biological systems contain a great deal of water, and then chemical changes will be brought about by both direct and indirect action. The possible role which indirect action can play had been largely neglected until 1942, when Dr Walter Dale working in Manchester showed that the 'activated water' could inactivate enzymes which are vital for the life of the cell. Later work showed that the free radicals which make up 'activated water' are capable of bringing about deep-seated chemical changes in all the vital constituents of the cell and must therefore be harmful for biological materials. For this reason the tendency to interpret radiation data on cells in terms of the target theory has become unpopular, and opinion has swung to the other extreme of considering free radicals from water as the main agent responsible for producing cellular damage. This tendency has probably gone too far, and chemical changes from direct action must play an important part. I shall refer to this again later.

RADIATION AS AN ANALYTICAL METHOD

The target theory's greatest usefulness at the present time lies in its analytical application for determining with ionizing radiations the size and shape of biologically active substances such as viruses. By irradiating under conditions where indirect action cannot occur (i.e. dry or frozen), fast-moving subatomic particles can be used as probes on the molecular level, because their path and path length are almost independent of the composition of the material through which they pass. They lose energy according to well understood physical principles, and the chance of an ionization occurring at any particular point in the irradiated material can be calculated. The ionization releases within a small volume an amount of energy which is so great that it is almost bound to bring about extensive chemical changes. Ionizing radiations can therefore be considered as destructive agents whose action is localized in submicroscopic areas smaller than that obtainable by any other method (for example it is quite impossible to get a beam of destructive ultra-violet light or a jet of toxic chemicals with a cross-section as small as that of the track of an ionizing particle). If a preparation of a biologically active material such as a virus is irradiated with a known dose of radiation, the number of ionizations occurring within the sample is readily calculated. Douglas Lea, a physicist working at Cambridge, pioneered this method and determined the sensitive volume of viruses, and when with the development of the electron microscope it became possible to photograph viruses it was seen that in many cases the sensitive volume deduced from irradiation experiments was identical with their total size, indicating that energy absorption anywhere within the virus led to its inactivation. In other cases the sensitive volume was found to be less than the total size, indicating that these viruses had an internal structure and that some parts were more vulnerable than others.

This kind of information could not be obtained in any other way, and in Lea's hands ionizing radiations had become an analytical tool. With the availability of new radiation sources capable of providing particles with a very wide range of ion densities this method was developed further at Yale University by another physicist, Ernest Pollard. Using different radiations the shape as well as the total volume can be calculated, and perhaps the most useful development is that the size and the shape of the parts responsible for different biological properties of the same virus can be determined. For example, a virus has the property of infection, and thereby brings about the disease, but it also has the ability to induce the body to form antibodies with which to counteract the virus. Once an animal has formed these antibodies it has become immune.

The ability of a preparation of the virus to infect is destroyed by much smaller doses of radiation than its property to produce immunity; from this the sizes of the parts responsible for these properties have been deduced. A vaccine is, of course, essentially a harmless preparation which causes the body to produce antibodies against an infective organism. The Salk polio vaccine is prepared by treating the virus with a chemical which destroys infectivity but does not completely remove its faculty to stimulate the body to make antibodies. It may be possible in some cases to use subatomic particles for the preparation of vaccines.

With some viruses Pollard has even been able to obtain an approximate idea of the relative positions occupied by the different elements responsible for the various properties in the virus. It may be possible to map out in this way where different biological functions are localized within the cell. The sensitivity of this analytical method is governed by the 'size of the probe' – that is by the volume over which the energy lost by ionization is spread; about this we have very little information at present, but we do know (see p. 204) that the chemical changes produced are not confined to the atom which is ionized and are spread to other molecules by energy transfer processes.

TARGET THEORY AND RADIOBIOLOGY

When it had been shown that the target theory explained satisfactorily the inactivation of viruses and in many cases gave surprisingly accurate values for their dimensions, the application of this concept over the whole domain of radiobiology seemed to be justified. In 1946 Douglas Lea published a remarkable book entitled *Actions of Radiations on Living Cells* in which he brought together the then available data and interpreted them on the basis of the target theory. This masterly presentation brought order out of chaos, and it appeared that the foundation for radiobiology had been firmly laid and that it remained only to fill in the details. Gene mutations appeared to fit all the mathematical requirements for a single-hit target; the number of mutations produced was independent of the rate at which the dose was applied, and varied in the correct way with the total dose received; the effectiveness of different radiations decreased with an increase in ion density. The sensitive volume of a gene calculated from these data gave a diameter of less than 0·01 μ. Since the gene is a hypothetical concept introduced by geneticists to explain heredity this value cannot be checked against one determined by direct physical methods, but indications from other types of experiments carried out more recently suggest that the gene is considerably larger than the value calculated.

The killing of bacteria and of a number of other types of cells was considered to be a single-hit phenomenon which brought about a lethal mutation. Radiation-induced mitosis delay could not be fitted into this scheme, since it depends to a greater extent on the rate at which the dose is given than on total dose; it is inherent in the target theory that the various events are quite independent of one another. Consequently it became necessary to separate arrest of mitosis from cell death and to attribute the former to some non-specific cumulative damage akin to systemic poisoning.

With the large-scale development of atomic energy and the availability of the new machines for the radiotherapy of cancer the number of workers engaged in research in radiobiology has increased greatly in the last ten years. This has led to the discovery of many new facts, and some of these new results cannot be reconciled with Lea's interpretation that gene mutations are brought about by a single-hit target mechanism and that the killing of cells is the result of a lethal mutation brought about in this way. Neutrons and other densely ionizing radiations were shown to be not less effective than X- or γ-rays, as demanded by theory, but were more effective in the production of mutations and above all in the killing of cells. Detailed work with bacteria also revealed that the relationship between dose and proportion killed is not necessarily the type required by a single-hit target process. Moreover, the shape of these curves which was believed to be characteristic could be altered by relatively minor changes of the conditions in which the bacteria were irradiated. It had long been known that radiation injury in mammals and other multicellular organisms could be repaired, but this, the protagonist of the target theory claimed, was due to complex recovery processes involving the whole animal and could not occur within a single cell. When the target is hit the cell dies, and there is no half-way house. This view became untenable when Alexander Hollaender found that by giving suitable treatments (see p. 174) after irradiation the number of bacteria killed by a given dose could be greatly reduced.

The simple and impressive interpretation of many radiobiological processes in terms of radiation hitting a specific target inactivated by one ionization cannot be maintained. In experimental science the discovery of new facts frequently – one might say almost invariably – makes it necessary to revise earlier theories which nevertheless served the invaluable purpose of co-ordinating facts and giving purposeful direction to the planning of new experiments. At present we have the sad situation that no theory has been advanced which encompasses satisfactorily the host of new facts found in the last decade, and the intellectually satisfying treatment of Lea has been replaced by chaos.

RELATIVE IMPORTANCE OF DIRECT AND INDIRECT ACTION

Inherent in the concept of the target theory is the assumption that the biologically important chemical changes were the result of direct action of the radiation and that the free radicals produced in water play no part. Absorption of energy by a vital chemical substance, for example the material making up the gene, was believed to be an irreversible event which could not be influenced in any way by changes in the external conditions. It is widely believed that only an effect produced by indirect action can be influenced by the amount of oxygen in the surrounding atmosphere, or the presence of added substances which act as protectors, or by freezing. How these factors modify indirect action has already been explained on p. 188 in terms of the chemical behaviour of the free radicals produced on irradiating water and their reaction with vital cell constituents.

The discovery six or seven years ago that almost all types of radiation injury, including such fundamental effects as gene mutation, breaking of chromosomes, and killing of cells, were greater in the presence than in the absence of oxygen gave the final blow to the attempt to explain them by a target mechanism, since it appeared to show that indirect action must be predominantly responsible for the biologically important chemical changes produced. This view is reinforced by the finding that certain chemicals, when present in the material at the time of irradiation, protect to some extent against many of the radiation injuries which seemed to be quite irreconcilable with direct action, while being readily explained by indirect action. Finally, experiments with seeds and pollen, which survive low temperatures, showed that radiation was much less effective below the freezing point than at room temperature, and this again pointed to the importance of indirect action.

The interpretations of these experiments, however, are not unambiguous but they do provide further proof that the injuries are not the result of hitting a definite target, since the *chance* of producing such an ionization cannot be influenced by external factors. The next step of the argument that the important chemical changes are produced indirectly does not necessarily follow. Experiments in model systems such as the irradiation of a solid, where the action can only be direct, have shown that the chemical changes produced are not the same in the presence as in the absence of oxygen, and in many cases oxygen exerts a greater influence on chemical reactions produced by direct action than by free radicals. A temperature effect has also been found for direct action; in many cases a greater proportion of the material is chemically changed when the irradiation is carried out at high than at low temperature under conditions where indirect action cannot occur. It is also possible to reduce the amount of chemical change produced by direct action by the admixture of another substance which can be considered a protector. The process of protection here is quite different from that which occurs when the action is indirect, since competitive removal of reactive intermediates can play no part. It seems likely that the energy initially taken up by one atom can spread almost instantaneously over short distances and be transferred in this way from one molecule to another if certain structural features are favourable. Similarly, energy absorbed initially in one part of a macromolecule may bring about a chemical change in another part. By side-tracking the energy in this way it becomes possible to protect against direct action.

From these experiments it is clear that direct action can be influenced by external factors, and that it is not necessarily true that all radiation effects which can be modified by changes in the environment must have been initiated by a chemical change produced by 'activated water'. The chemical events leading to a biological injury may be direct, even though protection is possible, and a reduction in temperature or oxygen concentration may lower the effectiveness of a given dose. The most likely situation is that both direct and indirect action contribute to the chemical changes which initiate radiation injury in a biological system. In mammals, and these, of course, concern us most, water forms between 70 and 85 per cent of the total weight (the value for man is about 75 per cent) and three-quarters of the total energy absorbed on irradiation will be taken up by water. A tempting deduction is that the bulk of the radiation effect is brought about by the products of irradiated water (i.e. by indirect action). This is an over-simplification, since two other factors have to be considered. Firstly, the water in the body is not uniformly distributed and there are parts where the water content is much lower.

All organs are not equally radiosensitive, and it may well be that harmful effects occur in the 'drier' regions. For example, there is much evidence to indicate that damage of the chromosomes plays an important part in changes which eventually affect the whole cell. The solid content of the chromosomes, which are jelly-like structures, may be many times greater than that of the cell as a whole, and an estimate of the part due to direct action based on the overall constitution of the entire cell would be quite misleading.

The second factor is that direct and indirect action may not be equally effective in producing the necessary chemical changes. In almost every case studied, a biologically active material is more readily inactivated by direct action if the calculation is based on the amount of radiation energy necessary to inactivate an individual unit. This was first noted by Lea, who found that tobacco mosaic virus, a plant virus on which much research has been done, was inactivated by one ionization if the action was direct, while in dilute solution in water it was necessary to produce on an average more than one thousand free radicals in the surrounding liquid before the virus was inactivated. Almost all these radicals will have reacted with the virus particle, but only about 1 : 1,000 of these reactions will inactivate while a single reaction produced by direct action invariably destroys the activity. The reason for this difference is that the products from activated water, being highly reactive, attack the virus wherever they happen to come in contact with it, and their reaction is consequently non-selective and largely confined to the surface. By direct action the radiation need not occur at the point of energy uptake, and transfer within the molecule can ensure its utilization at certain vulnerable points. When this virus is irradiated in solution inactivation will be predominantly by direct action until the concentration is less than one part of virus for every thousand parts of water. Under conditions prevailing in the cell the virus would be inactivated solely by direct action, since the other substances present would competitively remove free radicals formed in the water. The ratio of the efficiency of direct to indirect action is not so great if less complex substances are investigated, but it remains sufficiently large (i.e. seldom less than 10 : 1) to ensure that direct action plays an important part even when there is much water present. There is a possibility that gene mutations and breaking of chromosomes are the result of fracturing giant molecules of nucleic acid (see p. 216); if this reaction is studied with the isolated material it is found that direct action is at least fifty times more effective than indirect action and in the cell breakdown of nucleic acid would occur predominantly by direct action. In conclusion we can say that we do not know enough about the fundamental reactions preceding the biological injury to be able to estimate how much of the effect can be attributed to the reactions of the free radicals formed in water and how much to direct energy absorption by the substances of the cell. The experiments in model systems which show that direct action is much more efficient than indirect action indicate that under the conditions prevailing in the cell changes due to direct action must be very important.

RELATIVE BIOLOGICAL EFFECTIVENESS

All atomic radiations produce ionizations as they pass through matter, but the distribution of these events varies. With the densely ionizing α-particles a large amount of energy is lost in a small volume, while no ionizations occur over large regions of the irradiated material. With an equal dose of X- or γ-rays the same number of ionizations are produced, but they are distributed much more randomly; Figs. 14 and 15 illustrate this behaviour. For hitting a target which can be inactivated by one ionization the densely ionizing radiations will obviously be less effective, since the chance of missing altogether will be much greater (see Fig. 42). The same problem confronts the sportsman in deciding between a rifle and a shot-gun. Though the total explosive power may be the same the energy loss is different. A target capable of being killed by a small amount of energy is more likely to be brought down by shot which spreads its action over a greater area. In the less likely event of its being hit by a bullet the amount of energy used is greatly in excess of that necessary.

In the inactivation of viruses and enzymes and the other systems to which the target theory applies, radiations of low ionization density are more effective than α-rays or neutrons, because only one ionization – or in our analogy one pellet of shot – is necessary. In living systems the exact reverse applies. Densely ionizing radiations are much more effective in bringing about all the various types of injury, including both long-term effects like cancer and genetic damage, as well as radiation sickness and acute radiation death. Quantitatively this is expressed as the relative biological efficiency (abbreviated to RBE). If for a particular effect the RBE of α-rays to therapy X-rays is 4 : 1, this means that the dose of α-rays needed is one quarter of that which produces the same effect with X-rays. The greatest variation in efficiency occurs between α- and X-rays; the difference between ordinary X-rays (200 kV) and very hard X-rays is very much less. In other words the most marked differences are seen between radiations giving tracks with thousands of ionizations per μ and those with hundreds. The maximum difference observed between the efficiency of ordinary therapy radiation (i.e. 200 kV X-rays having 25 radiations per μ) and harder radiation (with 5 or 6 ionizations per μ) is at most 1·5 : 1, and is often less. The ion density from fast neutrons* which are given off in atomic explosions is about 300 ion pairs per μ and their biological effectiveness lies between those of α- and X-rays.

The RBE of different radiations is not a fixed number, but varies widely from one type of biological damage to another (see Table XI) and is in addition influenced by the condition of exposure. For example, the effect of hard radiations is less in the absence of oxygen than in air, while densely ionizing radiations are almost unaffected by the composition of the

* Fast neutrons themselves produce no tracks; these are made by the protons they eject from atomic nuclei (see p. 34).

TABLE XI

The relative biological efficiency (RBE) of different radiations

Biological effect	*Radiations compared*	RBE
Breaking of chromosomes in microspores	Neutrons: X-rays	4 : 1
Breaking of chromosomes in bean roots	α-rays: Neutrons: X-rays	8 : 6 : 1
Dose to kill mice (LD50)	Neutrons: X-rays	8 : 1
Dose to kill bacteria	α-rays: X-rays	0·2 : 1

$$\text{RBE} = \frac{\text{X-ray dose to produce desired effect}}{\text{Neutron (or }\alpha\text{-ray) dose to produce desired effect}}$$

atmosphere during irradiation. Consequently the RBE of neutrons to X-rays will be about three times as great in oxygen-free conditions as in air (see Fig. 43). Another important

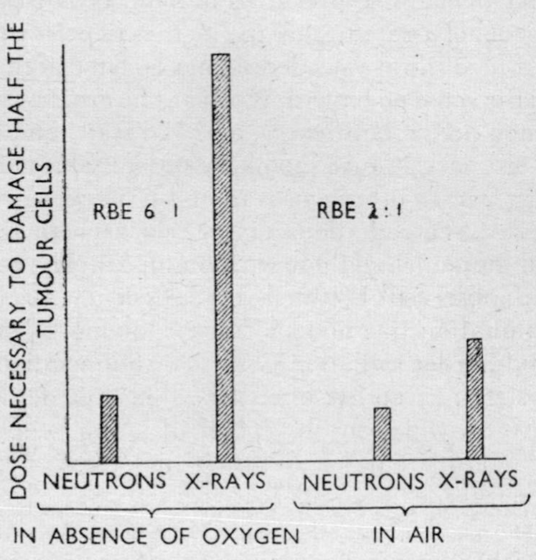

Fig. 43 – Comparison of the relative effectiveness of neutrons and X-rays in the presence and absence of oxygen.
(RBE stands for relative biological efficiency.)

factor is the rate at which a given dose is delivered. With X-rays and other hard radiation the extent of some injuries, notably arrest of cell division, decreases as the time taken to deliver the dose becomes greater, and often no damage can be seen if the exposure is spread over a sufficiently long time (e.g. Fig. 12). At very low intensities irradiation may even enhance growth rate: cell division of certain pollen grains was found to be temporarily stopped for about five hours by a dose of 200 r of X-rays if this was given over a period of less than ten hours. If the dose rate was smaller than about 20 r/hour no effect was observed. But with a dose rate of 6 r/hour, so that thirty-three hours were necessary to give the total dose of 100 r, cell division was enhanced. With densely ionizing radiation this time dependency is much less marked. This is well illustrated by an experiment in which bean roots were irradiated with a dose which was not sufficient to kill, but one which caused them to undergo a period of reduced growth rate lasting for about a week. The extent to which the growth is retarded is much greater if the X-rays are given at a high intensity than at a low intensity. With α-rays no such difference can be seen, and the RBE recorded will therefore be much greater if the dose is spread over a long period of time.*

Although an answer cannot yet be given why different radiations vary in their effectiveness in killing cells, there can be no doubt that the importance of high rate of loss of energy (i.e. densely ionizing tracks) is one of the most important clues in the search for the basic mechanism by which radiations interfere with life.

* A definite value cannot be quoted for the relative efficiencies of different radiations in producing radiation sickness. For specifying safe limits of exposure to radiation prudence demands that the largest value of the RBE be chosen for the conditions likely to be encountered. Consequently it has been assumed that fast neutrons are ten times as damaging as X-rays, and double this value is usually allowed for α-rays.

CHAPTER 10

HOW DO RADIATIONS WORK?

THE patient reader who has followed me through the preceding chapters will not be surprised that the way in which complex organisms are affected by radiations is not understood, and that the interplay of many factors makes it virtually impossible to relate the final injury to its cellular origin. What is more disappointing is that there is not yet a satisfactory theory which explains how relatively small doses arrest mitosis and kill individual cells some time after the irradiation is finished. Death follows immediately after extreme irradiation with hundreds of thousands of roentgen which causes widespread and readily recognized destruction. The real challenge is to discover the subtle process by which a minute amount of energy supplied by ionizing radiations can initiate changes which eventually result in cell death. The physical aspects of ionizing radiations, such as how and where they lose energy, are fully understood; in more recent years we have learnt what kind of chemical changes radiations produce; and in particular the nature of indirect action by highly reactive free radicals formed in water has been elucidated. Almost all the different constituents, including vital macromolecules such as enzymes and chromosome material, have been isolated, and the effect of radiations on them determined. Painstaking studies, in many cases using revolutionary new experimental techniques specially developed for these researches, have been made by biologists to follow the effects of radiation within the living cell. In the post-war years there has been no shortage of support for research into all aspects of the biological effects of ionizing radiations, and many scientists, including some in the forefront of their subject, have taken up this work. Yet, in the words of L. H. Gray: 'The story is as yet only fragmentary and the key discoveries lie ahead.

Herein lies its fascination to those who work in this field.' There are, however, some salient features which point to the direction in which the solution will probably be found.

BIOCHEMISTRY

In the living organism there is intense chemical activity; the most obvious is the 'burning up' of food to provide the energy necessary for all physical actions, such as the movements controlled by muscles. In the last two decades many of the individual chemical steps have been elucidated – often in great detail – by biochemists. The food is broken down in stages, each one controlled by one of the special macromolecules, usually proteins, which are known as enzymes, and in their presence chemical reactions take place between other substances which would not otherwise occur – or at least only very slowly. Each enzyme has the capacity for directing a certain specific process, but is not itself changed, so that it can go on doing this almost indefinitely so long as there is some of the substance – known as the substrate – whose reaction it controls. Many enzymes have been isolated and made to direct in the test-tube the same processes which they normally control in the cell, and in this way individual enzyme reactions have been studied in isolation.

The food must also supply the cell with precursors from which to make – again through the intervention of enzymes – the materials of which the cell is itself composed. This synthesis occurs not only in growing cells but also in the cells of adult animals, since the cell constituents are continually broken down and replaced (see p. 45). All these processes are vital if the cell is to survive, and it is very tempting to look for destruction of enzymes by radiation. Many chemical poisons act by putting out of action certain enzymes with which they combine. If the combination is loose, added substances can remove the poison from the enzyme and restore it to activity. A good example is the war gas lewisite, which was shown to inactivate certain enzymes by combining with their SH groups (see p. 187) which are necessary to their functioning. An antidote (known as BAL – British Anti-Lewisite) was discovered during the war which would prevent injury, if it was given soon after exposure, by removing the poison from the enzymes, which could then resume their function.

Two lines of evidence appeared to indicate that radiations might also act by destroying enzymes. Firstly, it was found that certain enzymes – again those containing the vulnerable SH groups – were apparently very sensitive to radiation, and exposure to quite small doses inactivated very dilute solutions of the pure enzymes which had been extracted from cells. What is more logical than that irradiation knocks out these vital cell constituents in the animal and that this leads to the observed radiation effects! Unfortunately, the position is more complicated; in the test-tube experiment the highly reactive free radicals produced by irradiation of water (see p. 184) must react with the dissolved enzyme, since no other substance is present to compete for them, and consequently the enzymes are very effectively inactivated. It had been forgotten that the cell is not a dilute solution of a pure enzyme, and that a multitude of other substances are present which react readily with the free radicals and compete for them with the enzyme. If the enzymes are irradiated in the presence of cellular material no significant inactivation can be detected except with doses which exceed many times those necessary to kill the cell.

Here a badly designed model experiment failed to provide any information. But experiments with irradiated organisms also proved misleading, for these appeared to show that many enzymes were inactivated since the processes they controlled occurred to a lesser extent. The eye, for example, shows a marked reduction in some SH enzymes after exposure to X-rays; since irradiation gives rise to cataract and cataract can also be produced by some poisons which inactivate SH enzymes, a correlation between these and radiation injury was again indicated. However, more detailed work showed that *immediately* after the irradiation there is no change in the activity of SH enzymes and a reduction is found only a day or so later. This proves that the inactivation of the SH enzymes was not a primary effect of the radiation but occurred at one of the later stages in the development of the injury. Recent researches have failed to reveal a single case where a reduction in enzymatic activity was found in a living organism immediately after irradiation; a certain time afterwards many enzyme-controlled reactions are reduced. This reduction is not the cause of the radiation sickness, but is an expression of the fact that the animal is ill.* Professor Krebs has pointed out that the majority of the enzymes in the cell are present in excess of requirement and that a substantial proportion of these could be lost without causing harm. When looking for the site of action of a very potent poison special attention should be paid to a very few special enzymes which occupy the position of pacemakers in the complex sequence of metabolic processes. By putting even quite a small proportion of such enzymes out of action quite a disproportionate amount of harm would be done. This possibility is certainly one that should be borne in mind, but there is no evidence that indicates that it plays a part in most radiation-produced injuries, since sparsely ionizing radiations are more effective than densely ionizing radiations in the inactivation of the enzyme, while the reverse is the case for cellular injuries. This applies equally to inactivation by the indirect action of free radicals and to inactivation by direct action. The relative biological effectiveness (RBE, see p. 207) of different radiations in bringing about cellular damage appears to exclude the possibility that the initial action is on enzymes themselves. But whatever this first vital chemical reaction may be, it very quickly initiates biological processes which result in a change in enzymatic reactions. For example, 100 r of X-rays given as a whole

* Reference has already been made to the few cases for which the apparently paradoxical finding has been well substantiated that some metabolic processes occur more rapidly immediately after irradiation than before (see p. 68).

body dose to a rat (about one-sixth of the lethal dose) significantly reduces the rate of metabolism of the spleen cells after one hour, but the maximum effect on the enzymes is only seen after a considerably longer time interval.

HIDDEN BARRIERS

We have already seen (p. 61) how the hypothesis of Douglas Lea, that radiations can only break chromosomes if they are crossed by a particle which produces at least twenty ionizations within it, can account for the higher effectiveness (RBE) of densely ionizing radiations. But this purely physical interpretation fails to account for many of the observed facts, and it seems clear that the production of chromosome abnormalities is an end-effect of radiation to which the general metabolism of the cell contributes, and that radiation only serves to trigger off the physiological processes involved. However, the general principle that radiations break down fine structures inside the cell is probably correct. Such barriers require a minimum amount of energy before they are broken, and consequently densely ionizing radiations are bound to be more effective than X- or γ-rays, and no better explanation has yet been put forward to account for the RBE of different radiations. Interference with internal structures would bring about an immediate amplification of a minute initial effect, since the cell contains its own means for destruction, such as enzymes which break down vital macromolecules, but normally internal barriers prevent the different components from coming into contact with one another. Once the enzymes have been released from their specific location they act extremely quickly, and injuries could become apparent within minutes. Radiation releases the floodgates and the dammed-up water does the rest.

The existence of barriers inside the cell is very strikingly revealed by photographs of cells taken with the electron microscope, which makes it possible to obtain magnifications of more than one hundred thousand times. Some are reproduced on Plates 6a and 6b. The light microscope (see Plate 3) has shown us that there are bodies in the cytoplasm of the cell, known as mitochondria, which are responsible for much of the biochemical activity of the cell, but only the electron microscope can show the organization of the still finer structures in the cell, known as the microsomes, with which many of the cell's enzymes are associated. These are complex structures with a whole network of membranes and if one of these were punctured enzymes would be released which then could upset the finely balanced organization of the whole cell. In the ordinary light microscope this fine structure was not seen, but since biochemists had proved that many complex reactions occur which are not associated with the readily visible mitochondria it was necessary to postulate that there must be some order there, and the Cambridge biologist Joseph Needham coined for it the term cytoskeleton, which the electron microscope has now revealed in a most impressive manner. This fine network of canals with enzymes located on the walls looks like the perfect conveyor belt for the manufacture of highly complex structures. There is good evidence that part at least of the cellular proteins are made here, and it seems a good 'machine' for the assembly of twenty or so different constituent amino-acids into a specific sequence involving many hundreds of them. The barriers retaining this structure are extremely thin and of molecular dimensions. The passage of an atomic particle through them could create havoc. The diversity of the end-effects of radiations, which is much greater than that found after poisoning with most chemical substances, would follow naturally if the initial effect were due to the coming together of cellular materials which are normally kept apart. Very many unrelated changes could then occur at the same time owing to damage in different parts of the cell. Subtle differences in radiation sensitivity between cells could easily arise, and the greater resistance of liver cells as compared to those of the spleen might be a reflection of stronger internal barriers within the cell; it would also follow that there were periods of resistance and sensitivity to radiation depending on the type of metabolic activity occurring in the cell at the time. This mechanism can apply both to actively dividing and to somatic cells, since both are continually engaged in synthesis and breakdown.

The problem is to find out which of the many cell barriers and structures are most easily broken by radiation, and here our attention should not be confined to the cytoplasm, as injuries in the nucleus could be equally if not more harmful, and, in particular, could cause the abnormalities seen in the chromosomes in cell division following irradiation. It may possibly turn out that in some cells damage in the nucleus, while in others damage in the cytoplasm, plays the predominant part, and the results of experiments with one type of cell need not necessarily apply to another.

THE NUCLEIC ACIDS

We do not know as yet the details of the fine structure of the nucleus of the cell in the 'resting' stage (see p. 45) when there is great biochemical activity including the synthesis of large molecules; during cell division the chromosomes can be seen, and they dominate the scene, but there can be no doubt that in the non-dividing cell there must be structures maintaining a high degree of order in the nucleus, as well as in the cytoplasm, but our techniques are so far inadequate to reveal them. The nucleus is highly vulnerable to atomic radiation and there is good evidence which suggests that for cells in active division the important initial radiation injury occurs there. The chromosomes are made up of a complex between proteins and giant molecules known as nucleic acids,* and the kind referred to as DNA

* There are two types of nucleic acid: ribosenucleic acid (RNA) and deoxyribosenucleic acid (DNA), which can readily be separated, and in most isolation processes the cellular nucleic acids are only obtained as these two fractions. All molecules of DNA and RNA are not the same, and there are many different varieties of each type, but so far no satisfactory method for their separation has been developed. The different types of both varieties of nucleic acid all have different biological functions, and there are many reasons for believing that the genetically important part of the gene is DNA.

may be particularly important for the genetic function of the chromosomes. While DNA is largely, if not wholly, confined to the cell nucleus, RNA occurs also in the cytoplasm. There is good, though not decisive, evidence that RNA is involved in the synthesis of protein. For example, the constituent amino-acids – or more probably one of their derivatives – may be lined up in their predetermined order along an RNA molecule where they are linked together by a suitable enzyme and finally come off the RNA which becomes available for further synthesis.

Much of our information concerning the role and position of the nucleic acids in the cell has been obtained with the ultra-violet microscope. By using light of different wavelengths it is possible to distinguish between substances having different chemical constitutions, and the relative positions of proteins and nucleic acids have thus been revealed (see Plate 16). Unfortunately this method cannot be used to differentiate between the two classes of nucleic acid, RNA and DNA.

Although the exact role of the nucleic acids remains to be discovered, there can be no doubt that they are key materials in the life of the cell, and, for this reason if no other, one would look for the role of radiation in them. One of the first and most unambiguous changes evoked by radiation is a marked decrease in the ability of the cell to synthesize DNA, and this becomes apparent within thirty minutes after irradiation. Without DNA synthesis the cell cannot divide, since chromosomes cannot be formed, and the radiation-produced delay in cell division seems a direct consequence of the arrest in DNA synthesis. Instances are recorded where irradiated cells continue to grow and attain unnaturally large dimensions but do not divide. Analysis showed that in these cases all the cell constituents continued to be produced normally after irradiation except DNA, which, however, is necessary for the doubling of the chromosomes without which cell division cannot occur. Since DNA is only made in the nucleus, this behaviour is consistent with those experiments which show that the critical injuries by small doses occur in the nucleus. The DNA-making mechanism is probably not knocked out by the radiation itself, since the decrease in activity is not observed immediately after irradiation, and it is tempting to speculate that the interference follows on the breakup of internal barriers and is a self-destruction. Unfortunately very little is known about the synthesis of DNA, and at the present time facts, not speculations, are required.

Damage to already formed nucleic acids would also be serious to the cell, since it seems probable that every molecule fulfils a special and unique role, and it is unlikely that there is an excess of nucleic acid over requirement, as there is for many enzymes. In fact nucleic acids may be in the same category as the pacemaking enzymes. The suggestion that damage to a nucleic acid molecule is the initial point of attack brings us again to the impasse that densely ionizing radiations are more efficient in producing cellular injury, while sparsely ionizing rays are more effective in inactivating nucleic acids. Reasons why chromosome breaks are unlikely to follow direct attack on the nucleoprotein gel have already been given in Chapter 2, and rather similar arguments also apply against the theory that the genetic effects of radiations are due to action of radiation immediately on the gene material. No satisfactory alternative mechanism has yet been proposed, but from general considerations it seems possible that injuries to the chromosome, and this automatically includes genetic damage, follow from the inhibition of DNA synthesis or are due to the release of enzymes – known to exist in the cell – which break down chromosome material.

WHAT USE IS IT?

Much research is done merely to satisfy the curiosity of the scientist, and many of the fundamental discoveries were made in the past by academic minds unconcerned with problems having immediate practical applications. The famous German physicist, Max Planck, claimed recently that in future also the really important new findings would follow so-called pure research unrelated to any possible application. The effect of radiations on living matter is certainly an intellectual challenge and as such worthy of purely academic study. However, I do not believe that basic problems cannot be tackled by those looking for direct application, and prefer the quotation from Pasteur which introduces this book. The study of radiation biology is a good illustration of this attitude, since from the very beginning the workers in it were concerned with solving practical problems. Here was the first method, other than surgery, which could effectively treat many types of cancer. The challenge to improve this tool unquestionably was and is the driving force behind most of the research. In recent years with the development of nuclear energy and the horror of nuclear warfare many new practical problems have to be solved. The dangers from radiation are in many respects quite different from those encountered from other injuries or toxic agents, and not even now do we know enough about them to lay down reliable and realistic safety limits. Practical needs and not a disinterested desire for knowledge stimulate this great volume of research. Yet this work perhaps more than any other is extending the boundaries of our understanding of the basic processes of life. The problem of how the minute amount of energy from small doses of radiation can drastically alter cells and whole complex organisms will not be answered until we know much more about how the cell functions, but it is research with radiations which is providing some of the most vital clues to the basic mechanisms of life.

CHAPTER 11

CHEMICALS WHICH PRODUCE THE SAME BIOLOGICAL EFFECTS AS ATOMIC RADIATIONS

In recent years a number of chemical substances have been found which produce biological changes that are very similar to and often indistinguishable from those produced by atomic radiations. Since they can be said to mimic radiations they are often referred to as 'radiomimetic' substances. A few have found practical application in the treatment of leukaemia, where they augment and sometimes even replace radiation and, for this reason, are usually administered by radiotherapists and are often considered as part of the field of radiobiology. A knowledge of the similarities and differences between the effects of the chemical agents and the radiations cannot fail to increase our understanding of the biological changes produced by both.

The discovery of radiomimetic properties arose directly out of wartime research on the chemical warfare agent, mustard gas, and the extension of this work to cancer treatment is an impressive example of turning swords into ploughshares. Well before the war a number of substances were known which, like radiations, could induce cancer, and which would stop cell division, but no chemical substances were known to produce genetic changes. Only radiations were believed to be able to cause gene mutations (see p. 114) which result in permanent changes, and much emphasis was placed on their uniqueness in this respect. When, in 1943, Miss Charlotte Auerbach produced conclusive evidence that mustard gas could induce true mutations this was a scientific discovery of the first magnitude, but few suspected that it pointed the way to improved methods for cancer treatment and the development of a new range of drugs.

Other similarities were soon discovered between the biological effects of radiation and mustard gas and a related chemical substance known as nitrogen mustard.* Chromosomes of plant and mammalian cells were broken by them, and the kinds of abnormalities seen appeared at first to be indistinguishable from those produced by radiation. An even more significant similarity was that cells were not sensitive to these chemicals during division, and chromosome breaks occurred only in the mitosis following the treatment. Chemicals, like radiations, also temporarily arrest cell division, which subsequently returns to normal if the amount of the chemical given is not too great. The radiation-like delayed effects differentiate the 'mustards' from ordinary poisons which kill cells at the time of administration. To injure cells before they divide, large quantities of 'mustards' are necessary. These experiments suggested that, at dose levels when they are not generally toxic, the mustards have a selective action on tissue containing rapidly dividing cells; indeed they harm mammals just as do atomic rays, and the first tissues to be affected are the blood-forming centres such as the bone-marrow, the genital organs, and expandable linings such as those of the stomach and intestine which are continually being replaced. Local greying of hair occurs at the site where they are injected, in the same way as after irradiation (see Plate 8a), and the pigment-producing cells of the hair are clearly highly sensitive to both types of agent.

The next step was to test the effect of the mustards on a number of animal tumours; they inhibited the growth of some, but failed to act on those which were also resistant to radiation. On the strength of these experiments the nitrogen mustard was used clinically shortly after the end of the

* Chemical formula for

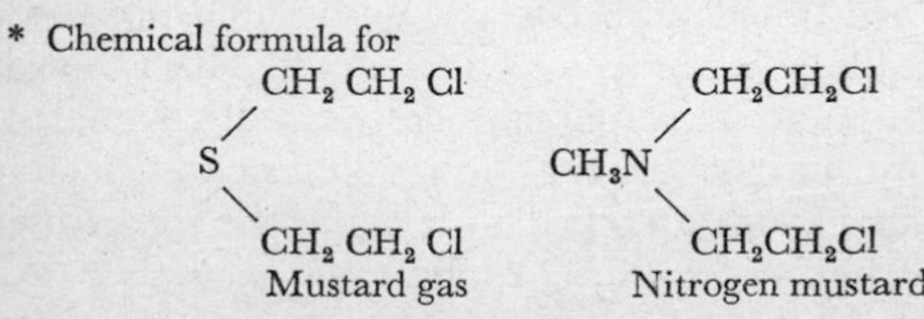

war and proved useful in some cases, but the results were not spectacular. However, these warfare agents opened up a new approach for research into the treatment of cancer by drugs, the full benefit of which has still to be reaped.

Unfortunately the similarity with radiations extends also to the ability to produce cancer; mustard gas, nitrogen mustard and many derivatives will produce malignant tumours in animals if given over long periods. Essentially all the different biological changes produced by radiation also follow treatment with these chemicals, but the observed injuries are the end of a sequence of changes, and the initial reactions which initiate the chain of events need not be the same in the two cases. The primary reactions of the radiomimetic chemicals with cell constituents are bound to be different from those produced by atomic radiations and it is not yet known at what stage in the development of the injuries seen the physical and chemical agents begin to run in parallel.

WHAT KIND OF SUBSTANCES ARE RADIOMIMETIC?

The development of a new drug usually comes about as follows: an empirical observation is made, either by chance or as a result of the routine testing of different substances, that a certain chemical compound produces a useful biological effect such as the reduction of blood pressure or the killing of dangerous bacteria. The chemists then make a whole series of related compounds to determine what are the essential features of the substance which make it active. Usually only certain groups are necessary, and these are then retained and combined with other groups. All these substances are tested until one is found which produces a useful result without unpleasant side-effects. This is how the different antibacterial sulphonamides were discovered; the sulphonamide part is responsible for killing the bacteria, while various groups attached to it make the drugs useful for different kinds of medical application.

The same technique was used in an attempt to find better compounds for cancer treatment than the original warfare agents. The activity depended on the presence of the chloroethyl group ($-CH_2CH_2Cl$) and high activity was found only if two of these were present in the same molecule. At the Research Institute of the Royal Cancer Hospital many hundreds of compounds containing this basic requirement were prepared and tested, and one or two of these showed very distinct practical advantages over the original nitrogen mustard and have found a definite place in the treatment of some cancers. When they act as effectively as radiation they are welcome, since the patient need not attend the hospital for treatment. Sometimes they produce results superior to those of radiation or act on tumours which no longer respond to radiotherapy. So far these improved results are limited, but they are sufficient to raise our hopes.

The chloroethyl groups are very reactive and combine with proteins and nucleic acids. Since their biological action was much more powerful when there were two of these reactive centres in the molecule, a group of scientists had the idea that they might act on the cell as crosslinking agents; that is, they bridged two large molecules together (see Fig. 44) by a firm bond so that they could not come apart again. Such a bridging reaction could cause the cell very great harm, and the possibility has been envisaged that chromosome breaks might be produced by linking together the two threads of a chromosome before it divides, so that at division a break must occur somewhere. In its most primitive form this theory is certainly not correct, although the possibility that a crosslinking process of some kind plays a part remains a very real possibility. The very great value of this suggestion lay in its stimulus to test a series of compounds for radiomimetic properties which would probably not otherwise have been examined. It has been known for many years that textile fibres – particularly rayon – could be greatly improved if the long molecules of which they are made are linked together. Consequently in the research laboratories serving the textile industry many compounds

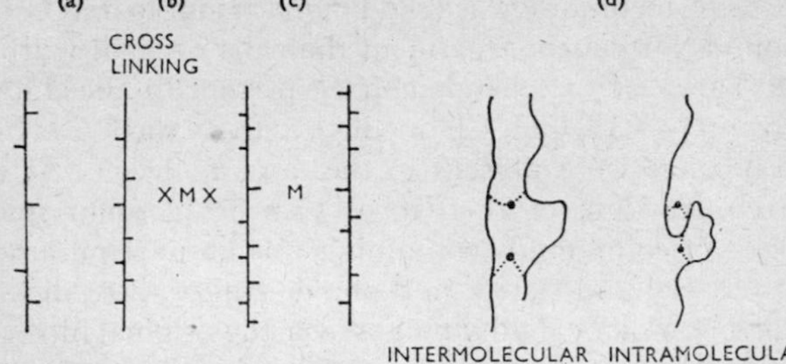

Fig. 44 – Crosslinking of Molecules.

(a) Two macromolecules; represent points with which a 'mustard' molecule can react.

(b) Mustard with its two reactive groups.

(c) Crosslinking reaction.

(d) The crosslinks need not be between different molecules but may join different parts of the same molecule together.

had been prepared and studied for their crosslinking properties, and a number of these were now tested for their biological action. In this way it was found that compounds containing two epoxides* or two ethylene imine* groups were also truly radiomimetic. Another line of research revealed that the presence of two mesyloxy groups* also rendered some compounds active, and one of them, known as 'Myleran', has found wide clinical application in the treatment of the chronic blood disease, myeloid leukaemia.

Although these new compounds have entirely different structures, they resemble the 'mustards' in that the centres responsible for biological activity are chemically very reactive and can combine with proteins and nucleic acids.

* Chemical structure of epoxide groups $-CH-CH_2$ (with O bridging CH and CH_2)

ethylene imine $-N-CH_2$ (with CH_2 bridging N and CH_2)

mesyloxy $-O.SO_2.CH_3$

Again, compounds with two of these active groups per molecule are, as a rule, very much more effective than those with only one.

HOW DO THEY WORK?

At first sight it is most surprising that compounds which have such completely different constitutions produce very closely related and well-defined biological effects, such as mutations, chromosome breaks, induction of tumours, and inhibition of growth, and there seems to be no parallel in other fields of chemotherapy. The only reasonable interpretation is that they owe their biological activity to the peculiar reactivity of their functional groups. This should give a most valuable pointer to their mode of action; but unfortunately they are capable of reacting with very many of the vital constituents of the cell so that, as in the case of radiations, one cannot deduce from test-tube experiments how they work in the body. In cases where the mechanism by which a drug acts is known, this has usually been discovered from so-called *in vitro* experiments (i.e. tests not involving animals) which revealed some highly selective behaviour.

How closely do the chemicals resemble radiation, and are there any reasons to assume that the primary process involves the same site in the cell? There are some indications that the intermediate stages in the development of the final injury may be different. While both act on the cell when it is in the resting stage and the damage to chromosomes becomes apparent only in subsequent divisions, the cell is at its most sensitive to radiation at the very end of the resting stage and to the chemicals at the beginning. Detailed analysis also shows that the chemicals most frequently cause a break in one particular region of the chromosome, while those from radiation occur more or less at random along its whole length. The relative frequency with which different mutations are produced also differs, as do a number of other features which are too technical to go into here. These variations do not, however, exclude the possibility that the radiomimetic chemicals initiate the processes leading to the cellular injuries by interfering with the same molecule or processes which are involved in radiations. The differences may be due to the fact that the chemicals will not act on the cell as uniformly as radiation since they have to diffuse in from the outside. This renders molecules near the cell membranes more susceptible than those on the inside. With radiation, of course, no such difference exists. Also the chemicals may not react immediately, and harmful substances may persist within the cell for many hours, and this is bound to introduce quantitative differences with radiations, which produce their chemical changes immediately. As with the radiations there is reason to believe that reactions in the nucleus of the cell are of special importance, although the cytoplasm is also affected and one of the most probable sites of reaction is with the vital processes controlled by the nucleic acids; but whether the interference is with the synthetic processes which give nucleic acids or with the nucleic acids themselves cannot be decided.

HUMAN HAZARDS FROM RADIOMIMETIC SUBSTANCES

The short-term effects are very similar to those from radiation and require no special mention; these substances must be treated with the same care that is extended to other powerful poisons. If a fatal dose is taken, death will occur some days later, just as with radiation, and so far no antidote has been discovered, though it seems likely that treatment with bone-marrow or spleen cells may help recovery in the same way as it does with radiation (see p. 175). With the long-term dangers the position is different from that with other poisons, and is comparable with the hazards from ionizing radiations. The mutations produced are as irreversible and as cumulative (see p. 121), and exposure of many people to small amounts of radiomimetic chemicals would be deleterious to the future of the whole population without noticeably affecting the individual. The damage would only appear in further generations and its extent is even more difficult to evaluate than for radiations. With the chemical it is impossible to get even an approximate idea; we cannot be sure which of the substances with which we come into contact will produce mutations. Probably relatively few people are exposed to the chemical agents which we definitely know to have this property, but it is certain that there must be very many more compounds which are active, but have not yet been found to be so in the laboratory. They may be present in polluted air, or we may come into contact with them through certain manufactured articles or foods. However, even if all the mutation-producing substances were known it would still be impossible to estimate how many mutations they actually produce in the population, since the proportion which actually get into the reproductive organs would vary from compound to compound; metabolic processes may favour the accumulation of some and prevent others from getting there. With radiations the position is much simpler once their intensity is known – and this can be done relatively easily; the dose received by the sex organs can be calculated.

Although we are ignorant about the extent of the genetic danger from chemicals we know after only a relatively short period of research in this field of many mutation-producing substances, and their diversity of structure makes one apprehensive about the true magnitude of the problem. Since determined efforts are now being made to limit the long-term hazards from exposure of many people to very small amounts of radiation, it would seem sensible to attempt to determine the extent of the danger from chemical substances, since it is at least possible that this may be more serious than the risk from atomic radiations. Yet this danger is nobody's special concern, and consequently no effort is made to attack the problem from the aspect of social hygiene.

Again, as with radiations, the radiomimetic chemicals

can give rise to cancer. Experiments indicate that both prolonged exposure to small doses, insufficient to produce any serious symptoms immediately, and treatment with one large dose from which apparent complete recovery had occurred, can produce cancer after a long period of time. Whether this makes an appreciable contribution to the incidence of this disease is not known. The experience with mustard gas in the 1914–18 war is reassuring. A careful analysis was recently carried out from the record of the Ministry of Pensions, which showed that there was no significant difference in the incidence of cancer at all sites* between those soldiers who had and those who had not been poisoned with mustard gas.

* The figures did show that the proportion of deaths due to lung cancer was greater in gassed soldiers, but it cannot be concluded that this is due to the cancer-producing action of mustard gas, since many of those exposed to it suffered for the rest of their lives from bronchial disorders. No difference is found in the incidence of lung cancer when the comparison is made between those gassed and those suffering disablement from bronchitis without having been exposed to mustard gas. The conclusion from this survey is that the increase in lung cancer observed in these cases is connected with bronchitis but not directly with mustard gas poisoning.

BIBLIOGRAPHY

I. BOOKS DEALING WITH ALL ASPECTS OF THE BIOLOGICAL EFFECTS OF IONIZING RADIATION

BACQ, Z. M., and P. ALEXANDER. *Fundamentals of Radiobiology.* (London: Butterworth, 1955)

HOLLAENDER, A. (ed.). *Radiation Biology,* Vol. I (in two parts). (New York: McGraw-Hill, 1954)

INTERNATIONAL CONFERENCE (GENEVA, 1955). *Peaceful Uses of Atomic Energy: Vol. II, Biological Effects of Radiation.* (United Nations, New York)

LEA, D. E. *Actions of Radiation on Living Cells.* (London: Cambridge University Press, 2nd ed., 1955)

SPEAR, F. G. *Radiations on Living Cells.* (London: Chapman and Hall, 1953)

II. IMPORTANT PUBLICATIONS WHICH DEAL IN DETAIL WITH THE SUBJECTS DISCUSSED IN THE INDIVIDUAL CHAPTERS

CHAPTER I

GRAY, L. H. 'The Distribution of ions, resulting from the irradiation of living cells', *British Journal of Radiology,* Suppl. No. 1, 1947

INTERNATIONAL CONFERENCE (GENEVA, 1955). *Peaceful Uses of Atomic Energy: Vol. 14. General Aspects of the Use of Radioactive Isotopes and Dosimetry.* (United Nations, New York)

MAYNEORD, W. V. 'Some Applications of Physics to Medicine', *British Journal of Radiology,* Suppl. No. 2, 1950

SEGRÉ, E. *Experimental Nuclear Physics.* (New York: Wiley, 1953)

SPIERS, F. W. *Radiation Absorption and Energy Loss by Primary and Secondary Particles.* Faraday Society Discussion No. 12, p. 13, (1952)

CHAPTER 2

Symposium on Chromosome Breakage; Supplement to *Heredity,* Vol. 6, 1953

Ciba Foundation Symposium, *Ionizing Radiation and Cell Metabolism.* (London: J. and A. Churchill, 1956)

GLÜCKSMANN, A. 'Biological Levels of the Radiosensitivity of Somatic Cells', *British Journal of Radiology,* 1954, **27**, 660

HEVESY, G. VON. *Symposium on Radiobiology.* (New York: Wiley, 1952)

KOLLER, P. C. *Chromosome Breakage; Progress in Biophysics,* Vol. 4, (London: Pergamon Press, 1954)

ZIRKLE, R. E., and W. BLOOM. 'Irradiation of Parts of Individual Cells', *Science,* 1953, **117**, 487

CHAPTER 3

The Effects of Atomic Weapons. (New York: McGraw-Hill, 1950)

BEHRENS, C. F. *Atomic Medicine.* (Baltimore: Williams and Wilkins, 1953)

BLAIR, H. A. *Biological Effects of External Radiation.* (New York: McGraw-Hill, 1954)

CONARD, R. A. 'Response of Human Beings Accidentally Exposed to Significant Fall-out Radiation', *Progress in Radiobiology,* p. 491. (London: Oliver and Boyd, 1956)

ELLINGER, F. P. 'Effects of Ionizing Radiation on Growth and Replacement of Hair', *Annals of New York Academy of Sciences,* 1951, **53**, 682

ELSON, L. A. 'Comparison of the Physiological Response to Radiation and to Radiomimetic Chemicals', *Radiobiology Symposium* 1954, p. 235. (London: Butterworth, 1955)

HURSH, J. B., and G. W. CASARETT. 'The Lethal Effect of Acute X-irradiation on Rats as a Function of Age', *British Journal of Radiology,* 1956, **29**, 169

JAPANESE SCIENCE COUNCIL. *Research in the Effects and Influences of the Nuclear Bomb Tests.* (Tokyo: Ueno, 1956)

MOLE, R. H. 'Whole Body Radiation – Radiobiology or Medicine', *British Journal of Radiology,* 1953, **26**, 234

OUGHTERSON, A. W., and S. WARREN. *Medical Effects of the Atom Bomb in Japan.* (New York: McGraw-Hill, 1956)

QUASTLER, H. 'The Nature of Intestinal Radiation Death', *Radiation Research,* 1956, **4**, 303

RAJEWSKY, B. 'Radiation Death in Mammals', *Radiobiology Symposium,* 1954, p. 81. (London: Butterworth, 1955)

UPTON, A. C. 'The Pathogenesis of the Haemorrhagic State in Radiation Sickness', *Blood,* 1955, **10**, 1156

UPTON, A. C., F. P. CONTE, G. S. HURST, and W. A. MILLS. 'The Relative Biological Effectiveness of Fast Neutrons, X-rays and γ-rays for Acute Lethality in Mice', *Radiation Research,* 1956, **4**, 117

CHAPTER 4

The Hazards to Man of Nuclear and Allied Radiation. (London: H.M. Stationery Office, 1956)

'International Commission on Radiological Protection Recommendations', *British Journal of Radiology,* N.S. Suppl. No. 6, (1955)

GUSTAFSSON, A. 'Mutation Research in Plants', *Acta Agriculturae Scandinavica,* 1954. **4,** No. 3

HADDOW, A. (ed.). *Biological Hazards of Atomic Energy.* (Oxford University Press, 1952)

MULLER, H. J. 'Our Load of Mutations', *American Journal of Human Genetics,* 1950, **2,** 111

NATIONAL ACADEMY OF SCIENCES. *The Biological Effects of Atomic Radiation.* (Washington, 1956)

NATIONAL ACADEMY OF SCIENCES. *Effect of Exposure to the Atom Bombs on Pregnancy Termination in Hiroshima and Nagasaki.* (Washington, 1956)

RUSSELL, L. B., and W. L. RUSSELL. 'Radiation Hazards to the Embryo and Foetus', *Radiology,* 1952, **58,** 369.

(Also excellent review articles in *Peaceful Uses of Atomic Energy,* Vol. II, and *Radiation Biology,* Vol. I, see general part of Bibliography.)

CHAPTER 5

BRUES, A. M. 'Ionizing Radiation and Cancer', *Advances in Cancer Research,* Vol. 2, p. 177. (New York: Academic Press, 1954)

BURGHER, I. C., I. COURSAGET, and J. F. LOUTIT (ed.). *Progress in Nuclear Energy – Medical Sciences.* (London: Pergamon Press, 1956)

CASE, R. A. M. 'Cohort Analysis of Cancer Mortality in England and Wales, 1911–54 by Site and Sex', *British Journal of Preventive and Social Medicine,* 1956, **10,** 172

FURTH, I., and A. C. UPTON, 'Histopathologic and Carcinogenic Effects of Ionizing Radiation', *Annual Review of Nuclear Science,* 1953, **3,** 303

FURTH, I., and A. C. UPTON. 'Late Effects of Experimental Nuclear Detonation in Mice', *Radiology,* 1954

INTERNATIONAL CONFERENCE (GENEVA), 1955. *Peaceful Uses of Atomic Energy; Vol. 10. Radioactive Isotopes and Nuclear Radiation in Medicine.* (United Nations, New York)

KAPLAN, H. S. 'Indirect Induction of Lymphomas in Irradiated Mice', *Cancer Research*, 1956, **16**, 422

KAPLAN, H. S. 'Inhibition of Lymphoid Tumours Development by Shielding and Partial Body Irradiation of Mice', *Cancer Research*, 1951, **11**, 261

LACASSAGNE, A. *Les Cancers produits par les rayonnements corpusculaires; Actualités scientifiques et industrielles, No. 981.* (Paris: Harmann, 1945)

LAWRENCE, J. H., and C. A. TOBIAS. 'Radioactive Isotopes and Nuclear Radiations in the Treatment of Cancer', *Cancer Research*, 1956, **16**, 185

LORENZ, E. 'Radioactivity and Lung Cancer; a Critical Review of Lung Cancer in Miners of Schneeberg and Joachimsthal', *Journal of National Cancer Institute*, 1944, **5**, 1

CHAPTER 6

(Very full discussion of chemical protection in *Fundamentals of Radiobiology*, see general part of Bibliography)

ALEXANDER, P., and Z. M. BACQ. 'Mode of Action of some Substances which Protect against the Lethal Effects of X-rays', *Radiation Research*, 1955

BACQ, Z. M., and A. HARVE. 'Protection of Mice Against a Lethal Dose of X-rays by Cyanide, Azide and Matmonitoile', *British Journal of Radiology*, 1957, **24**, 617

GRAY, L. H., A. D. CONGER, M. EBERT, S. HORNSEY, and O. S. A. SCOTT. 'The Concentration of Oxygen Dissolved in Tissues at the Time of Irradiation as a Factor in Radiotherapy', *British Journal of Radiology*, 1953, **26**, 638

HOLLAENDER, A., G. E. STAPLETON, and F. L. MARTIN. 'X-ray Sensitivity of *E. Coli* as Modified by Oxygen Tension', *Nature*, 1951, **167**, 103

PATT, H. M. 'Protective Mechanisms in Ionizing Radiation Injury', *Physiological Reviews*, 1953, **33**, 35

CHAPTER 7

COLE, L. J., M. C. FISHLER, and M. E. ELLIS. 'Studies on the Nature of the Radiation Protection Factor in Mouse Spleen', *Radiology*, 1955, **64**, 201

FORD, C. E., J. L. HAMERTON, D. W. H. BARNES, and J. F. LOUTIT. 'Cytological Identification of Radiation – Chimaeras', *Nature*, 1956, **177**, 452

HENSHAW, P. S. 'Effects of Repeated Small Doses of X-rays', *Journal of National Cancer Institute*, 1944, 4, 513

HOLLAENDER, A., and R. F. KIMBLE. 'Modification of Radiation Induced Genetic Damage', *Nature*, 1956, 177, 726

HOLLAENDER, A., and G. E. STAPLETON. 'Modification of Radiation Damage after Exposure to X-rays', *British Journal of Radiology*, 1954, 27, 117

JACOBSON, L. O. 'Evidence for a Humoral Factor Concerned in Recovery from Radiation Injury', *Cancer Research*, 1952, 12, 315

KAPLAN, H. S., M. B. BROWN, and J. PAULL. 'Influence of Bone-marrow Injection on Involutions and Neoplasia after Irradiation', *Journal of National Cancer Institute*, 1953, 14, 303

LORENZ, E., C. CONGDON, and D. UPHOFF. 'Prevention of Irradiation Induced Lymphoid Tumours by Spleen Protection', *Journal of National Cancer Institute*, 1953, 14, 291

CHAPTER 8

Radiation Chemistry, Faraday Society Discussion No. 12 (1952)

ALEXANDER, P., and A. CHARTESBY. 'Physico-chemical Methods of Protection against Ionizing Radiation', *Radiobiology Symposium* 1954, p. 49 (London: Butterworth, 1955)

BURTON, M. *Symposium on Radiobiology*. (New York: Wiley, 1952)

DALE, W. M. 'Modern Trends in Radiation Biochemistry', *Actions chimiques et biologiques des radiations*. (Paris: Masson, 1955)

LEA, D. E. 'The Action of Radiation on Dilute Aqueous Solutions', *British Journal of Radiology*, Suppl. 1, 1947

CHAPTER 9

ALEXANDER, P., and A. CHARLESBY. 'Energy Transfer in Macromolecules Exposed to Ionizing Radiation', *Nature*, 1954, 173, 578

EVANS, T., and C. EVANS. 'The Influence of Quantity and Quality of Radiation on the Biological Effect', *Symposium on Radiobiology*. (New York: Wiley, 1952)

GRAY, L. H. 'Comparative Studies of the Biological Effects of X-rays, Neutrons and other Ionizing Radiations', *British Medical Bulletin*, 1946, 4, 11

LEA, D. E. 'The Inactivation of Viruses in Relation to the Mechanism of Biological Actions of Radiations', *British Journal of Radiology*, Suppl. No. 1, 1947

POLLARD, E. C. *The Physics of Viruses.* (New York: Academic Press, 1954)

POLLARD, E. C. 'The Action of Ionizing Radiation on Viruses', *Advances in Virus Research,* Vol. 2 (New York: Academic Press, 1954)

CHAPTER 10

(See all the books listed in the general Bibliography)

'Symposium on Physiological Effects of Radiation at the Cellular Level', *Journal of Cellular and Comparative Physiology,* 1952, **39**, Suppl. 2

ALEXANDER, P., and K. A. STACEY. The 'Production of Hidden Breaks in DNA', *Progress in Radiobiology,* p. 105. (London: Oliver and Boyd, 1956)

CHARGAFF, E., and J. N. DAVIDSON. *The Nucleic Acids,* Vols. 1 and 2. (New York: Academic Press, 1955)

DAVIDSON, J. N. *The Biochemistry of the Nucleic Acids.* (London: Methuen, 1953)

ERRERA, M. 'Action of Ionizing Radiation on Cell Constituents', *Radiobiology Symposium,* 1954, p. 93. (London: Butterworth, 1955)

HEVESY, G. VON. 'On the Effects of Roentgen Rays on Cellular Division', *Reviews of Modern Physics,* 1945, **17**, 102

CHAPTER 11

ALEXANDER, P. 'The Reactions of Carcinogens with Macromolecules', *Advances in Cancer Research,* Vol. 2, p. 1. (New York: Academic Press, 1954)

BOYLAND, E. 'Mutagens', *Pharmacological Review,* 1954, **6**, 345

CASE, R. A. M. 'Mustard Gas Poisoning, Chronic Bronchitis and Lung Cancer', *British Journal of Preventive and Social Medicine,* 1955, **9**, 62

HADDOW, A. 'The Chemotherapy of Cancer', *Medical Treatments and Principles,* (ed. Evans). (London: Butterworth, 1953)

HADDOW, A. 'Biological Alkylating Agents', *Physiopathology of Cancer* (ed. Homburger and Fishman). (New York: Hoeber-Harper, 1953)

INDEX

Index

Index

Some Pelican books
on allied subjects are described
on the remaining pages